We are sure there will be
plenty of stories about
" Stan Howell of Maenclochog "
in future editions!
Happy 60th and beyond.
John & Eve

MORE PEMBROKESHIRE FOLK TALES

VOLUME FOUR
OF THE FOLK TALES TRILOGY

Brian John

GREENCROFT BOOKS
Newport, Pembrokeshire, SA42 0QN

Printed in Wales

GREENCROFT BOOKS

MORE PEMBROKESHIRE FOLK TALES

First Edition 1996

Published by Greencroft Books, Trefelin, Cilgwyn, Newport, Pembs SA42 0QN. Tel/fax 01239 -- 820470

DEDICATION

To my wife Inger after 30 years of happy marriage, with thanks for endless support and encouragement, sound advice, and many fascinating days out and about in Pembrokeshire. And to our sons Stephen and Martin, in the hope that they too will find pleasure in the simple tales and gentle humour of this old county.

Designed by Brian John

Typeset by Brian John and Inger John, using Palatino 11 pt font and Claris Works software on Apple Mac LC475 computer

Printed in Wales by Gwasg Gomer, Llandysul

Cover illustration from a painting by the author

The story illustrations come from the following nineteenth-century children's annuals: *The Boy's Own Paper, The Girl's Own Paper, Sunday, Gleanings from Popular Authors Grave and Gay, Punch* and *Harper's Young People.*

ISBN 0 905559 73 8

CONTENTS

		Page
Preface		7
Introduction		8
Glossary of Welsh Terms		10
The Sources of the Stories		12
The Story Locations		15

Section One: Tales of the Saints — 17

1.1	St Teilo and the King of Dimetia	18
1.2	Caradog and the Dogs	20
1.3	The Return of St Teilo's Skull	21
1.4	St Govan and the Bell	22

Section Two: Heroic Deeds — 23

2.1	Slaughter on Cardigan Bridge	24
2.2	The Old Warrior at Waterloo	25
2.3	William Nichol the Martyr	27
2.4	Across the Ocean to Abercastle	28
2.5	Love at Ffair Gurig	30
2.6	The Broth of the Broth	32
2.7	The Wreck of the Treasure Galleon	33

Section Three: Strange Happenings — 35

3.1	The Gold Ring on the Mountain	36
3.2	Fox Hunt at Freystrop	37
3.3	The Hound of the Scourfields	39
3.4	The Society of Sea Serjeants	40
3.5	Sir John and the Cargo of Salt	41
3.6	Leekie Porridge and the Silver Buckles	43
3.7	Incident at Freshwater East	44
3.8	The Legend of Bedd Morris	46
3.9	The Last Wreckers at Pendine	47
3.10	Tragedy at Hangstone Davy	48
3.11	The Wrecking of the St David's Bell	49
3.12	The Last Pembrokeshire Smuggler	50
3.13	The Gold Hoard of Y Cwrt	52
3.14	The Coins of Llangwarren	53
3.15	Duel at Withybush	54

Section Four: Fairy Tales   55
4.1	Strange Arrival at Cardigan	56
4.2	The Fairies at Pentre Ifan	57
4.3	The Wandering Cobbler of Nolton	58
4.4	Fairies at Caerfarchell	60
4.5	The Fairy King and Queen	61
4.6	Fairy Helpers for Dr Harries	62

Section Five: Witchcraft and Magic   63
5.1	The Queen of the Pembrokeshire Witches	64
5.2	The Hound of Hell at Hayscastle	65
5.3	In Trouble with the Law	67
5.4	The Case of the Missing Cows	68
5.5	Rescue on Frenni Fawr	70
5.6	Gwen Davies the White Witch	71
5.7	Nasty Fright at Pen Palis	72
5.8	The Flying Witch of Marloes	74

Section Six: Signs, Omens and Portents   75
6.1	Spirit Funeral at Cresswell Quay	76
6.2	The Corpse Candles at Pendine	77
6.3	Fetch Funeral at St David's	78
6.4	Mr Severn meets the Ceffyl Pren	79
6.5	Jumping to Conclusions	80
6.6	Fetch Funeral for a Minister	82
6.7	Phantom Funeral at New Hedges	83
6.8	The Haunting of John Mathias	84
6.9	Corpse Candle at Walton West	85
6.10	The Haunted Bell	85
6.11	No Place for Horses	88
6.12	Presentiment in Tenby	88
6.13	All Hallow's Eve in a Country House	89

Section Seven: Ghostly Tales   91
7.1	Ghostly Rebuke in Newport	92
7.2	The Lavender Lady of Newport Castle	93
7.3	The Ghost in the Crypt	94
7.4	The Black Monk of Caldey Island	95
7.5	The Ghost of Maesgwynne	96
7.6	The Saintly Lady of Rhos-y-Gilwen	98

7.7	Ghostly Visit at Stepaside	99
7.8	Three Ghostly Ladies of Llandawke	100
7.9	The Parson's Home Brew	101
7.10	The UFOs at Nevern	103
7.11	The Ferocious Housekeeper	104
7.12	Strange Events at Bush House	106
7.13	The White Lady of Gosport House	106
7.14	The Faceless Phantom of Cosheston	107
7.15	The Haunted Bridge	108
7.16	The Tenby Ghosts	109
7.17	The Ghost of St Florence	110
7.18	The Ghostly Pirate Ship	111
7.19	The Ghostly Monks of St Buttock	113
7.20	The Bwcci Bal at Cilgerran	114
7.21	Ghostly Events in the Castle Inn	116
7.22	The Great White Whale at Strumble Head	117
7.23	The Hauntings at Merlin's Bridge	119
7.24	Ghostly Funeral in Haverfordwest	120

Section Eight: Folk Heroes Great and Small — 121

8.1	Strange Men on the Mountain	122
8.2	Callican and the Donkeys	125
8.3	How Hemmy Saved the Bacon	126
8.4	Value for Money	128
8.5	The Boss knows Best	128
8.6	Georgie's Trip to Market	129
8.7	Not actually Needed	130
8.8	A Nice Lie In	130
8.9	The Cancer Healers of Cardigan	131
8.10	Isaiah and the Beautiful Trout	134
8.11	The Breaking of the Logan Stone	136
8.12	Squire Hammett and the Tin Works	137
8.13	The Record Breakers of Pendine	139
8.14	Heroism in Ramsey Sound	140
8.15	A Symbolic Gesture	142
8.16	Order of Priorities	143
8.17	A Need for Caution	143
8.18	A Blessed Mistake	144

When their day's work had come to an end, the workmen were happy enough to share out the coins which were left behind.
See story 3.14

PREFACE

This book is, if you will excuse the expression, the fourth volume in The Pembrokeshire Folk Tales Trilogy. The first three books, namely **Pembrokeshire Folk Tales** (1991), **The Last Dragon** (1992), and **Fireside Tales from Pembrokeshire** (1993) were very well received by Pembrokeshire people and by visitors, and taught me that there is a deep and abiding interest in the folk traditions and history of the old and new county. . Further, I have been encouraged by many readers to continue the process of collecting together our old stories, many of which have never been published in an accessible modern format.

The flow of material for this series of books appears almost inexhaustible. That having been said, I am aware that supplies of some types of tales are now drying up; for this volume I have found it quite difficult, in spite of exhaustive research, to find new fairy tales and new tales about local magicians, witches, mermaids and fearsome beasts. In compensation I have discovered many new tales of ghosts, strange omens, and heroic deeds, and it has been a pleasure to discover a number of fascinating tales of hidden treasure. And there is still a wealth of material in the literature relating to local characters, extraordinary events, and natural and unnatural phenomena.

All the stories in this volume are "genuine" in that they have all come from previously published sources or from telephone calls, casual conversations or letters sent in by helpful local people. I have not invented a single story; that would be a most improper thing for a folk tale collector to do. At the end of each story I have cited my sources, just in case any reader wishes to follow up or research particular topics in more detail. With the publication of this volume the total number of tales recorded in the "Folk Tales" project reaches 433 -- a far higher total than was ever anticipated when I started work in 1990.

I thank all those who have helped in the production of this book, and in particular the staff of the reference section of Pembrokeshire County Library in Haverfordwest; Jonathan Lewis and his colleagues at Gwasg Gomer for their friendly and efficient printing service; and the many individuals (some of whom wish to remain anonymous) who have sent me material. Finally I thank my wife Inger for her constant support and encouragement, and for her help with typing, design and proof reading.

INTRODUCTION

On the following pages there are 95 Pembrokeshire folk tales not previously published in this series of books. Following the warm reception given to the first three volumes of The Folk Tales Trilogy, I have decided to keep to a well-tried formula. The book is therefore divided into eight sections. We begin with a section entitled Tales of the Saints (4 tales), followed by a section on Heroic Deeds (7 tales), and a section on Strange Happenings (15 tales). Then follows a group of 6 Fairy Tales and a section on Witchcraft and Magic (8 tales). Next comes a section of 13 strange tales on Signs, Omens and Portents, and a group of 24 traditional Ghostly Tales. In the final section of the book there are 18 tales of Folk Heroes Great and Small, which are difficult to classify elsewhere. I have to assume that all of the tales recounted here are true, or almost true! However, some of the tales at the end of the book need, I suspect, to be taken with a large pinch of salt......

In my research for this book I have been pleased to discover a number of "lost" tales about hidden treasure amid the press cuttings held in the Pembrokeshire County Library. These old tales are difficult to classify, and are included in the most appropriate sections of the book. Examples are stories 2.7, 3.13, and 3.14. As in previous volumes, there is a glossary of Welsh terms, a comprehensive bibliography, and a listing of story locations.

A word about my sources. As with the earlier volumes, the most important sources have proved to be local historians and clergymen who were obsessed with local folk tales and folk traditions at the end of the last century and the beginning of this one. I have found the press cuttings collection in the Pembrokeshire County Library to be a wonderful source of material, and there are certainly undiscovered treasures which still reside in the depths of the large-format folders and files which are so carefully protected by the library staff. Mary John and her staff (and previous librarians and their staffs) deserve our thanks for the way in which this valuable resource grows year by year and week by week, with a classification system that enables researchers to hunt for -- and frequently find -- their particular treasures.

The most important collections of West Wales folk tales remain those of William Howells, J Ceredig Davies, Meredith Morris, Wirt Sikes, and Marie Trevelyan. But now we can add to these, as a result of studies in the press cuttings collection, the names of Francis Green, Francis Jones, and JW Phillips. These three, between them, collected a vast amount of material, including their own reminiscences and many folk tales obtained by talking to elderly Pembrokeshire people. They wrote innumerable articles for the local papers in the early part of this century, and it is a tragedy that hardly any of these have previously appeared in book form.

Those who wish to delve deeper into the world of Pembrokeshire folklore and folk tradition will be pleased to know that several of the key sources have recently become available in reprint form; the books by Edward Laws, Richard Fenton, Mary Curtis, William Howells, Wirt Sikes, Evans Wentz and J Ceredig Davies are now on sale in bookshops and libraries, thanks to Llanerch Publications and Dyfed CC Cultural Services Dept. It is to be hoped that this good work will be carried on by the new Pembrokeshire County Council.

Finally, it is worth reminding ourselves what folk tales are actually for. Throughout the past five years of work on the Folk Tales Project I have been impressed over and again by the frailty of mankind and by the simple morality of Pembrokeshire tales. The traditional tales, with many local variations, have been used down through the centuries in order to teach children (and adults!) how to behave and to strengthen the civilised values of town and country people. As we have seen before, wickedness is always punished, whereas the virtues of honesty, kindness, truthfulness, and generosity are always rewarded. And interestingly enough, the same appears to be true of the brand new stories which are circulating in Pembrokeshire at this very moment, even in the hard and commercial world of the late Twentieth Century.

Brian John
October 1996

GLOSSARY OF WELSH TERMS

Aderyn y Gorff: a corpse bird, harbinger of death.
Afanc : a water monster, or alternatively a beaver.
Annwn : land of fairies, the underworld or otherworld.
Awenyddion: poets who speak while in a trance.
Bwbach: a goblin able to transport people through the air.
Bwca: a helpful household goblin or spirit.
Canwyll Gorff : corpse candle, a light denoting a death or the
    passage of a funeral.
Ceffyl Dwr : a small beautiful spectral horse or other
    supernatural animal.
Ceffyl Pren: a wooden horse carrying the effigy of some guilty
    person.
Coblin: a goblin, a "knocker spirit" in mines or caves.
Consuriwr : a magician or man with special or supernatural
    powers.
Crefishgyn : a spirit.
Cwn Annwn : the hounds of Hell, corpse dogs or sky dogs.
Cyfaredd : charm, fascination, spell.
Cyfarwydd : a skilled teller of stories.
Cyhyraeth : death omen, generally heard but not seen; spectre;
    phantom funeral.
Cythraul : devil.
Diawl : devil.
Draig: dragon or winged serpent.
Drychiolaeth : apparition or spectre.
Dyn hysbys : a wise man or wizard (literally : a knowing one).
Dynon bach teg : fairies (literally : fair little folk).
Ellyll : elf or goblin.
Gwenhudwy : mermaid or sea divinity.
Gwraig hysbys: witch.
Gwyddon : hag, witch or sorceress.
Gwlad y Tylwyth Teg : Fairyland
Gwrach : hag, witch.
Gwrach y Rhybyn: screaming banshee.
Gwylnos : vigil or wake.
Hiraeth: longing or nostalgia for Wales.
Hudol : magician or sorcerer.
Noson Lawen : "merry evening" of light entertainment.

Plant Rhys Ddwfn : fairies dwelling on the invisible islands off the Pembrokeshire coast (literally: children of Rhys the Deep).

Rheibio : to curse or bewitch.

Simnai fawr: big open fireplace or inglenook.

Tan ellyll : will o' the wisp, dancing light over boggy ground.

Tanwedd : death omen in the form of a falling light.

Toili : a phantom funeral.

Tolaeth : death omen such as a tolling bell or the sound of coffin-making.

Tylwyth Teg : fair folk or fairies.

Ychen bannog : oxen of the spirit world, connected with water stories.

Ysbryd drwg : evil spirit or devil.

THE SOURCES OF THE STORIES

BENNETT, T. 1982 **Welsh Shipwrecks, Vol 2**, Laidlaw-Burgess, Haverfordwest, 63 pp.

BIELSKI, A. 1979 **Tales and Traditions of Old Tenby**, Five Arches Press, 108 pp.

BRINTON, P. & WORSLEY, R. 1987 **Open Secrets**, Gomer, 196 pp.

BROMWICH, R. 1961 **Trioedd Ynys Prydain (The Welsh Triads)**, Univ of Wales Press, Cardiff, 555 pp.

CARRADICE, P. 1992 **Pembroke - for King and Parliament**, Pembroke Town Council, 100 pp.

COLYER, R. 1987 **The Teifi: scenery and antiquities of a Welsh river**, Gwasg Gomer, 91 pp.

CURTIS, M. 1880 **The Antiquities of Laugharne, Pendine, and their Neighbourhoods**, republished 1991, Dyfed CC, Carmarthen, 339 pp.

DAVIES, J.C. 1911 **Folk-lore of Mid and West Wales**, Welsh Gazette, Aberystwyth, 341 pp. (reprinted by Llanerch Publishers 1992)

EVANS WENTZ, W.Y. 1911 **The Fairy -Faith of the Celtic Countries** (Reprint 1981), Humanities Press, Bucks, 524 pp.

EVANS, A. & WILLIS, W. 1987 **Folk Tales and Superstitions of the Vale of Neath**, Gwasg Morgannwg, Neath Abbey, 32 pp.

FENTON, R. 1811 **A Historical Tour through Pembrokeshire**, London, 388pp. (reprinted by Dyfed CC 1994)

GALE, J. 1992 **The Maenclochog Railway**, Milford Haven, 75 pp.

GEOFFREY OF MONMOUTH, 1150 **The History of the Kings of England** (trans. Lewis Thorpe 1966), Penguin, 373 pp.

GIRALDUS CAMBRENSIS, 1188 **The Journey through Wales** (trans. Lewis Thorpe 1978), Penguin, 333 pp.

GODDARD, T. 1983 **Pembrokeshire Shipwrecks**, Hughes, Swansea, 198 pp.

HALL, S.C. and A.M. 1861 **The Book of South Wales**, reprinted 1977 by EP Publishing, Wakefield, 512 pp.

HOWELLS, R. 1968 **The Sounds Between**, Gomer, Llandysul, 192 pp.

HOWELLS, R. 1977 **Old Saundersfoot**, Gomer, Llandysul, 133 pp.

HOWELLS, R. 1984 **Caldey**, Gomer, Llandysul, 261 pp.

HOWELLS, W. 1831 **Cambrian Superstitions**, Longman, London, 194 pp. (reprinted by Llanerch Publishers 1991)

JAMES, D.G. 1957 **The Town and County of Haverfordwest,** J.W. Hammond, Haverfordwest, 172 pp.

JAMES, D.W. 1981 **St David's and Dewisland,** Univ of Wales Press, Cardiff, 228 pp.

JOHN, B.S. 1979 **Honey Harfat: a Haverfordwest Miscellany,** Greencroft Books, Newport, 65 pp.

JOHN, B.S. 1995 **Pembrokeshire: Past and Present,** Greencroft Books, 256 pp.

JOHN, T. 1994 **Sacred Stones,** Gomer, 64 pp.

JONES, E. 1978 **Folk Tales of Wales,** Gomer, Llandysul, 135 pp.

JONES, F. 1953 "Family Tales from Dyfed", **Trans. Hon. Soc. Cymm.,** p 61.

JONES, G. & JONES, T. 1976 **The Mabinogion,** Dent, London, 273 pp.

JONES, Ll. 1980 **Schoolin's Log,** Michael Joseph, 224 pp.

JONES, T.L. & JONES, D.W. 1993 **Cancer Curers -- or Quacks?** Gomer, 128 pp.

JONES, T.G. 1930 **Welsh Folk-Lore and Folk Custom** (Reprint 1979), Brewer, Cambridge, 255 pp.

LAWS, E. 1888 **The History of Little England Beyond Wales,** Bell, London, 458 pp. (reprinted by Dyfed CC 1995)

LEWIS, M. 1996 **Newport Pem and Fishguard,** Archive Photographs Series, Chalford Publishing, 128 pp.

McKAY, K.D. 1989 **A Vision of Greatness,** Chevron, 397 pp.

MASON, R. 1858 **Tales and Traditions of Tenby,** Tenby and London, 50 pp.

MILES, D. 1983 **A Pembrokeshire Anthology,** Hughes, Llandybie, 269 pp.

MILES, D. 1984 **Portrait of Pembrokeshire,** Hale, London 223 pp.

MILES, D. 1995 **The Ancient Borough of Newport in Pembrokeshire,** Dyfed CC, 144 pp.

MORRIS, M. 1899 **The Folklore of South Pembrokeshire,** microfiche held in Pembrokeshire County Library. (ms No 4.308, Cardiff Central Library)

PARRY-JONES, D. 1988 **Welsh Legends and Fairy Lore,** Batsford, London, 181 pp.

PHILLIPS, W.D. 1926 **Old Haverfordwest,** J.W. Hammond, Haverfordwest, 121 pp.

PUGH, J. 1986 **Welsh Ghosts and Phantoms,** Emeralda, 112 pp.

PUGH, J. 1987 **Welsh Witches and Warlocks,** Gwasg Carreg Gwalch, Llanrwst, 120 pp.

RAGGETT, P. 1990 **Solva**, Pearce, Milford Haven, 44 pp.

REES, J.Rogers 1897 "Pembrokeshire Fairies", **Wales IV**, pp 15 - 17.

REES, N. 1992 **St David of Dewisland**, Gomer, Llandysul, 37 pp.

RHYS, J. 1901 **Celtic Folklore : Welsh and Manx (2 Vols)**, Oxford, 717pp.

RICHARDS, W.L. 1992 **Changing Face of Haverfordwest**, Civic Society, Haverfordwest, 150 pp.

ROBERTS, A. 1974 **Myths and Legends of Pembrokeshire**, Abercastle, 32pp.

SIKES, W. 1880 **British Goblins** (Reprint 1973), E.P. Publishing, Wakefield, 412 pp. (reprinted by Llanerch Publishers 1991)

SPENCER, R. 1991 **A Guide to the Saints of Wales and the West Country**, Llanerch, Lampeter, 112 pp.

THOMAS, W.J. 1952 **The Welsh Fairy Book**, Univ. of Wales Press, Cardiff.

TIMMINS, Thornhill 1895 **Nooks and Corners of Pembrokeshire**, Elliot Stock, London, 197 pp.

TREVELYAN, M. 1909 **Folk-Lore and Folk-Stories of Wales**, Stock, London, 350 pp.

VAUGHAN, H.M. 1926 **The South Wales Squires**, Methuen, London, 216 pp.

WILKINS, C. 1879 **Tales and Sketches of Wales**, Owen and Co, Cardiff, 383 pp.

WILLIAMS, D. 1955 **The Rebecca Riots**, Univ. of Wales Press, Cardiff, 377 pp.

WORSLEY, R. 1988 **The Pembrokeshire Explorer**, Coastal Cottages of Pembrokeshire, Abercastle, 127 pp.

Note: all of the Newscutting files referred to in the "story sources" on the pages that follow are held in the Haverfordwest County Library (Reference Section) and are available for research on the library premises.

THE STORY LOCATIONS

Abercastle 2.4
Amroth 6.4

Broad Haven 3.10, 6.11
Broadway 3.10
Brynberian 8.4
Burton 8.16

Caerfarchell 4.4, 8.3
Caldey Island 1.4, 3.6, 7.4
Cardigan 2.1, 4.1, 8.9
Carew 3.5, 8.8
Carew Newton 5.1
Carmarthen 4.6, 5.4
Carningli 3.8
Carn Bica 31
Castell Malgwyn 8.12
Cilgerran 7.6, 7.20
Cosheston 7.14
Cresswell Quay 6.1
Crymych 5.5
Cwm Gwaun 3.13, 7.9
Cwrt 3.13
Cwrt-y-Cadno 5.3, 5.4

Dinas 3.8, 4.6

Fishguard 7.22
Frenni Fawr 5.5
Freshwater East 3.7
Freystrop 3.2

Hayscastle 5.2
Holyland 5.1
Haverfordwest 1.2, 2.2, 2.3, 3.4,
        6.11, 7.3, 7.15, 7.25, 8.7

Lamborough Moor 6.11

Laugharne 6.2, 7.13
Little Haven 4.3
Little Milford 7.23
Llandawke 7.8
Llandeilo 1.1, 1.3, 5.3
Llandeloy 6.10
Llangwarren 3.14
Llechryd 8.12
Llanychaer 3.13
Lochmeyler 6.10

Maesgwynne 7.5
Manorbier 3.12, 5.6
Marloes 5.8, 8.6
Mathry 8.5, 8.16
Merlin's Bridge 1.2, 7.23
Milford 3.5
Morfabychan 3.9
Mynydd Preseli 3.1

Narberth 2.6, 6.5, 7.21
New Moat 3.3
Newport 2.5, 3.8, 7.1, 7.2, 7.11, 8.1
Nevern 2.5, 7.10
Nolton 4.3

Pembroke 3.5, 7.12
Penally 1.1
Pencaer 2.7
Pendine 3.9, 6.2, 8.13
Pen Palis 5.7
Pentre Ifan 4.2
Pill 7.19
Pontfaen 3.8, 7.9
Pwll Deri 2.7

Ramsey Sound 8.14
Rhos 7.15

Rhos-y-Gilwen 7.6

St Botolp's 7.19
St David's 3.11, 6.3, 8.14, 8.18
St Florence 7.17
St Govan's 1.4
St Nicholas 8.10, 8.11
Saundersfoot 6.4, 6.7
Slebech 7.15
Solva 8.2
Stepaside 7.7, 8.15

Strumble Head 7.22
Swanlake 3.12

Tenby 3.6, 6.5, 6.12, 7.16, 7.18
Treffgarne 4.3
Treindeg 6.10
Twy Cross 6.7

Walton West 6.9
Werndew 4.6
Withybush 3.15

CAREW CASTLE.

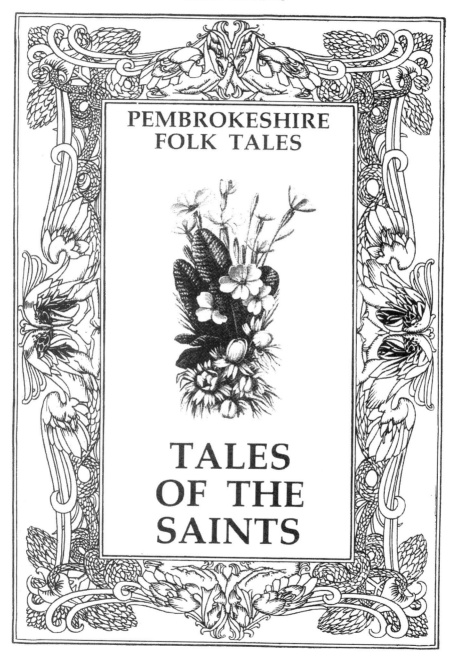

PEMBROKESHIRE
FOLK TALES

TALES
OF THE
SAINTS

1.1 St Teilo and the King of Dimetia

Teilo was one of the three most famous saints of Pembrokeshire (the others being Dewi and Padarn). They were also referred to in the old Welsh triads as the three "blessed visitors of the Isle of Britain" since they were the most perfect of guests; they were saintly and humble, demanded little or no comfort, taught the Gospel to those who wished to hear it, stayed with equal pleasure in the homes of the nobility and the peasantry and of natives and strangers, and never expected reward, food or drink in exchange for the blessings which they brought to their hosts. If only all ones's guests could be so accommodating .....

Teilo was born at Penally and became a disciple of Dewi Sant at Glyn Rhosyn (close to the site of the present cathedral and city). He travelled widely with Dewi and Padarn, and the three of them made a mythical journey to Rome and the Holy Land that is reputed to have lasted seventeen years. On his return to Wales he became a great missionary and cleric in his own right, and founded monasteries and churches in Llandeilo (Carmarthenshire), Llandeilo Llwydarth

..... *arguments and even fights broke out among the guests and soldiers so that at least one person was killed each evening.*

near Maenclochog, and Llandaff in Cardiff. His fame spread far and wide, and in the centuries following his death in 560 AD his followers dedicated many other churches to his memory.

Once upon a time, towards the end of Teilo's life when he was at his monastery in Penally, Aircol Lawhir the son of Tryfun was king of Dimetia. He held his court at a place called Liscastle, which was the metropolis for the region. However, the king was greatly troubled because every night, following the serving of meat and drink in the royal hall, arguments and even fights broke out among the guests and soldiers so that at least one person was killed each evening. The king realised that the demon drink was responsible for this state of affairs; but he was apparently too weak a king to cut the alcohol ration!

At last he determined to take action. First he commanded the court to fast and pray for several days. And then he called for Teilo to come from Penally. The saintly cleric duly arrived with two of his disciples named Iouil and Fidelis, and he left them in charge of the kitchen and the wine cellar. With the king's steward out of the way, the two brothers distributed meat and drink in sufficient quantities "to all by measure". Excess was eliminated, and all became content. With nobody inflamed by drink, quarrels ceased, and no more murders were committed. The king decided that this miraculous transformation in his affairs had been affected by Teilo by the grace of the Holy Spirit; and so pleased was he with the reduction in the local death rate that he gave Teilo three villages in South Pembrokeshire. One was near St Florence, another was near Trefloyne, and the third may have been Amroth.

Date: c 555 AD   *Source: Mason p 107*

1.2 Caradog and the Dogs

St Caradog was the last of the Welsh saints, and he is the saint most closely associated with Haverfordwest. He was born in Brecon and spent much of his time in South Glamorgan and on the Gower Peninsula. Stangely, his destiny in life was quite closely associated with dogs. When he was a young man, before he became a wandering cleric, he was employed as a musician in the court of Rhys ap Tewdwr, the prince of South Wales. He enjoyed a carefree life, but then he lost two of the prince's prize dogs, and his master was so angered that he dismissed him from his post. He became a pilgrim, then trained as a monk, and spent much of his later life as a hermit in various peaceful places.

As an old man he was driven from his little cell on one of the Pembrokeshire islands by the Norman invaders, and came to Haroldston, near Merlin's Bridge. The precise location of his cell is not known, but it was probably near "Cradock's Well", a healing spring in the valley of the Merlin Brook, on the edge of the old Portfield Common. Apparently a road was built over the spring in 1842, after which the flow of water was carried in a culvert. Portfield Fair owes its origin to the healing spring, for in the Middle Ages it was a popular place of pilgrimage.

One local episode involving hounds occurred around 1120. Caradog was very friendly with young Richard Fitz Tankard, the son of the castellan of Haverfordwest castle, who used to bring him provisions and spend happy hours talking to him about the wonders of the world. On one occasion the boy had a pack of hounds with him, and he was overtaken by a thunderstorm and a deluge of rain as he approached the hermit's cell. He ran inside to find shelter, but the dogs got into a panic and ran about wildly. The boy called and whistled, and even tried to tempt them by offering them food, but he could not get them under control. But St Caradog took charge of the situation. He smiled at the boy, made a gentle motion with his hand, and the panic-stricken hounds all became calm, trotted towards him, and sat down at his feet. This episode, and various others, gave the holy man a reputatiuon not unlike that of St Francis of Assisi.

Date: c 1120   *Source: Spencer p 20; Laws p 139*

1.3 The return of St Teilo's Skull

The strange story of St Teilo's Skull was told in Volume I of this series (story 3.6). There is an interesting sequel. The skull, reputed to have been that of St Teilo, had healing powers and could work wonders for those who used it as a recepticle for drinking the waters of St Teilo's Well. Initially it was looked after by the Mathew family, who were the traditional "keepers of the tomb of St Teilo" in Llandaff Cathedral in Cardiff. In 1658, when William Mathew died childless in Llandeilo, the skull passed into the ownership of the Melchior Family, but it was sold -- and apparently lost -- in 1927.

An intriguing twist in the story arises out of an old prophecy apparently made in 1658 by an old woman of Llandeilo when William Mathew died. She is reputed to have said: "Misfortune will fall on the house of Mathew for over 200 years, and then the skull of Teilo will be restored to the last male of their line and their luck will turn again, and those that kept the skull will get a double blessing." For eight generations the Mathew family lived in Ireland, and a branch then moved to Australia. Naturally enough, the family was rather interested in the old prophecy, and in the late 1800s Archbishop Arnold Mathew traced the whereabouts of the skull. It was a member of the family, one Gregory Mathews, who purchased the skull for £50 in 1927.

After that the skull's whereabouts were unknown for some years, with a number of people in Cardiff and Pembrokeshire taking up the hunt. But then the Australian branch of the Mathew family wrote to the Bishop of Llandaff. They informed him that the skull was in a bank vault in Sydney, and expressed a wish to restore it to Llandaff Cathedral. They travelled with it to Wales, and on St Teilo's Day in 1994 it was received back into the cathedral in a special ceremony involving branches of the Mathew family from Hong Kong, Australia and the UK, Mr and Mrs Alven who now own the old sacred site of St Teilo's Well at Llandeilo, and the Bishop of Llandaff. It now rests in the reliquary of St Teilo's Chapel within the cathedral. It is somewhat more elaborate than it was, having been mounted on the tips of silver angels wings on a blackwood base, with silver gilt pieces affixed to the lip of the skull fragment.

Date: 1994   *Source: Rev Brian Lodwick*

1.4 St Govan and the Bell

There are many legends associated with the Church of St Govan's. One is perhaps related to the name of the saint - the name "Gobhan" means "smith". After an active life as a cleric and missionary he travelled to Rome and then ended his days as the abbot of a monastery in County Wexford. He retired to a life of contemplation here in the narrow cleft in the limestone cliffs of South Pembrokeshire. Maybe he built the chapel with his own hands around 590 AD.

According to legend Gobhan the smith made a fine silver bell with his own hands, and hung it in the little bellcote at the west end of the chapel. There it served to ring out praise to God and also to warn sailors off the coast of the proximity of land when thick fogs swirled around the cliffs. One night a band of pirates stole the bell, and so distraught was poor St Gobhan that he prayed for divine retribution to fall upon the heads of the wrongdoers. A great storm blew up, and the pirate vessel, with the bell on board, was wrecked on the rocky coast. Providentially, the silver bell was conveyed by a band of angels from the wreck back to the site of the chapel; but instead of restoring it to the bell-tower they entombed it in a limestone rock. For centuries afterwards this particular rock, when struck with a hammer, miraculously resonated like a silver bell.

In another version of the legend the pirates, having stolen the bell, were active in the area around Caldey Island. They lured a vessel onto the rocks by lighting fires designed to look like the approach lights to Tenby Harbour. Unknown to them, the vessel carried the Abbot of Caldey, and when it foundered on the rocks a crimson-breasted bird rose from the wreck and carried the soul of the saintly abbot to Heaven. The pirates were terrified out of their wits, and shortly afterwards their own vessel was wrecked in a storm with the loss of all hands. And so the silver bell sank to the sea-bed, where it still rings faintly for those who have the faith to hear it.

Date: c. 590   *Source: Press Cuttings, Vol 28 (1938) p 74*

PEMBROKESHIRE
FOLK TALES

HEROIC
DEEDS

2.1 Slaughter on Cardigan Bridge

One of the bloodiest battles of the early Middle Ages occurred on the north bank of the Teifi River at Cardigan, probably in 1136. The political situation in Ceredigion was extremely complicated at the time, but the main cause of the battle was the anarchy which followed the death of King Henry I in 1135.

Cardigan town was founded around 1110 by Gilbert de Clare, who was given license by the king to subdue Ceredigion following the outrageous and unruly behaviour of Prince Owain, son of Cadwgan. (It was this impetuous prince who had abducted Princess Nest, the wife of Gerald of Windsor, Constable of Pembroke Castle.) Gilbert constructed a massive stone castle close to the river, with a small township clustered around its ramparts. To assist in the defence of the castle and colonial settlement he built a fine wooden bridge (just upstream of the present bridge) which would allow easy access between the north bank of the tidal river and the Barony of Cemais to the south, which was under firm Norman control. The situation appeared quite stable, even after the death of Gilbert de Clare, for his son continued to rule Ceredigion with a rod of iron. But then, after the death of Henry, there was a power vacuum, and various Norman barons started to form temporary and fragile alliances, feather their nests and even plunder their Norman neighbours.

The Welsh princes realised that their Norman enemies were now vulnerable. So they began to rally their forces, starting in the Welsh "heartland" of Gwynedd. As the rebellion built up, Earl Robert, the Lord of Cardigan, was killed in an ambush. Then Owain and Cadwaladr, the sons of Gruffydd ap Cynan of Gwynedd, attacked from the north and swept through Ceredigion. They destroyed several castles en route, and were joined by many local chieftains and their men. The Normans received news of the attack, and immediately mustered their forces from Cemaes, Emlyn and Cardigan. Many soldiers crossed the bridge to Cardigan, and other reinforcements were sent from the Flemish colony of South Pembrokeshire. At last a substantial defensive force of several thousand men was assembled in and around Cardigan and under the control of Stephen, the Constable of the Castle.

The battle, when it came, was short and decisive. The armies met at Crug Mawr, north of the river. The Welsh on this occasion were well prepared, well equipped, and well led. The Normans were confronted by about 6,000 foot soldiers and 2,000 armoured horsemen, and were routed in the first attack. The Welsh mounted an initial assault with showers of arrows and spears and followed it with a blood-curdling cavalry charge. The Normans broke ranks and fled back towards the river. Such was their terror that many of them surrendered to women and children in the streets of the town, begging to be provided with shelter and protection. The bulk of the fleeing army reached the castle and the bridge. But the castle gate then had to be shut to keep out the Welsh, and thousands of soldiers scrambled and fought to cross the flimsy wooden structure across the river. Such was the weight of the fleeing army that the bridge collapsed. Those who were lucky were suffocated or drowned. Most were slaughtered among the fractured timbers by their pursuers.

According to legend, so terrible was the slaughter on and around the bridge that the river ran red with blood, and so numerous were the corpses that a new bridge was formed of human flesh, enabling the last of the fleeing army to cross, dry-shod, to the safety of the south shore. Over 3,000 of the Normans and their mercenaries were killed in the battle. and there is a local tradition that the large mound at Crug Mawr is the place where Norman corpses were piled high and then covered with earth to create a grotesque memorial to one of the greatest Welsh victories in the turbulent history of West Wales.

Date: 1136   *Source: Lewis 1990 p 1; Warner p 78*

2.2 The Old Warrior at Waterloo

One of Haverfordwest's most distinguished sons was General Sir Thomas Picton, who was a great leader and Wellington's right-hand man during the Peninsular War. He was born in the town house of the Laugharne family in Hill Street, subsequently converted to become the Dragon Hotel. He was educated in Haverfordwest Grammar School, which at that time was near the entrance to St Thomas' Church. He was determined from an early age to become a soldier, and obtained an ensign's commission in the Thirteenth Foot when he was only thirteen years old. After studying at a military academy he served in Gibraltar and then the West Indies, making such a reputation there that he was appointed Governor of Trinidad in 1797 -- the year of the "French Invasion" back home in Pembrokeshire.

In Trinidad he made a fine reputation as a humane and efficient administrator, and on being transferred to Portugal to take part in the military campaigns of the Peninsular War, his qualities of leadership were soon recognized by the Duke of Wellington, who made him second-in-command. He was a good friend and a formidable enemy who could be quite ruthless in the pursuit of his objectives. But he always shared the dangers and hardships that his men faced, and became something of a father figure for most of them. He fought fiercely for them both on and off the field of battle -- for example in the matter of obtaining food supplies and weapons when the supply lines were dangerously stretched.

He gained a reputation of being a highly unconventional general, both in his military tactics and in his attitude to dress. He once said that he did not mind how his soldiers looked so long as they minded their fighting. He occasionally went into battle wearing an old top hat and a shabby great-coat, with an umbrella under his arm if the weather was inclement.

After the Peninsular War he returned to West Wales, but when Napoleon escaped from Elba Wellington sent for him and he was soon back in the thick of the fighting. He was given a secret commission appointing him commander-in-chief of the allied forces in the event of Wellington's death or disablement. At Quatre Bras on 16th June 1815 he was badly wounded; but with broken ribs and in severe pain he kept the full extent of his injuries secret. Two days later, at Waterloo, he was killed while repulsing one of the most serious French attacks of the day. His last words were reputedly "Charge! Hurrah! Hurrah!" He was buried in the family vault in London, and a memorial was set up for him in St Paul's Cathedral.

Date: 1815   *Source: Maxwell Fraser 1956*

2.3 William Nichol the Martyr

At the top of High Street in Haverfordwest is a granite memorial to one William Nichol, one of only three Protestant martyrs in Wales. He was burned at the stake near this spot on 9th April 1558. Not much is known about him, but his biggest crime seems to have been a lack of flexibility, for most of the people of Pembrokeshire (including the clergy) managed to adapt without too much difficulty to the comings and goings of Catholicism and Protestantism.

But with the accession to the throne of Queen Mary, Protestants were forced to renounce their faith, and one of those who refused was Robert Ferrar, Bishop of St David's, who was burnt at the stake in Carmarthen in 1555. Three years later Mary (who became known as "Bloody Mary") ordered another purge, and the new Catholic Bishop of St David's, Henry Morgan, had to find a burnt offering. He chose William Nichol, "a poor half-witted creature" who passed his time delivering orations on street corners in the county town. These discourses, which caused the locals much amusement, sometimes related to theological matters; and since he appeared to take pleasure in attacking whatever happened to be the dogma of the day, it was not difficult to accuse him of heresy. So he was taken into custody and condemned, and died a dignified death in a blazing inferno while tied to a stake in the middle of High Street. The locals were appalled, and could see no reason why this man, who was "so simple a good soul that many esteemed him half foolish", should die for a cause that he so clearly did not understand.

A stone marked the spot of the martyrdom for many years, but was later removed to Dale Castle. The red granite monument was put up in 1912. Some years afterwards a deep hole was discovered by workmen in the middle of the road about 15 yards downhill from the site of the memorial. This was undoubtedly the hole that held William Nichol's stake.

Date: 1558   *Sources: James, p 35; Laws, p 270*

2.4. Across the Ocean to Abercastle

On Saturday 10th August 1876 the people of Abercastle were surprised to see a little sailing boat, in a very battered condition, entering the creek from the open sea. The boat was of an unusual design, and proved to be a 18-foot American dory of the type used for fishing on the Grand Banks of Newfoundland. At the helm was an emaciated figure in ragged clothes. He seemed on the point of collapse, and after tying his boat to a buoy the locals helped him ashore. The sailor introduced himself as 24-year old Alfred Johnson. He said that he had sailed across the Atlantic Ocean in 46 days, having left Shake Harbour, Nova Scotia, on 25th June. His voyage was the first recorded single-handed crossing of the Atlantic.

After providing the sailor with some dry clothes and getting some food and drink into him, the locals crowded round to hear his story. Unfortunately Alfred proved to be an exceptionally shy and modest young man, and it was only with some difficulty that the facts of the matter were extracted from him.

Apparently he was a fisherman by profession. He lived in Gloucester, a fishing port not far from Boston. One day he conceived the idea of sailing to Liverpool, partly to prove that the fishermen who worked the Grand Bank were among the best sailors in the world, and partly to celebrate the centenary of the United States. His ancestors had come from Liverpool, and he decided that he would like to visit various relatives there before returning to the USA (with his boat) by cargo ship in time for the Centenary Exhibition.

Although friends and family tried to talk him out of his planned adventure, Alfred was determined to press ahead. At Gloucester he fitted out his fishing boat and added a foredeck to provide shelter for his provisions. He raised the sole and made it watertight, and ballasted the boat with iron. (Later, this proved to be a bad mistake, for the iron affected his compass so that he was never quite sure of his position or his sailing direction.) He re-named the boat **Centennial**. Then, with only about 18 inches of freeboard and hardly enough room for him to stretch his legs among the stores, sails and ropes, he slipped quietly out of Gloucester on 15th June. He sailed over the Grand Bank to Nova Scotia and entered Shake Harbour on 22nd June. He spent three further days making adjustments to his sails and rigging, and taking on more stores. Then, disregarding the dire warnings of the old sailors on the waterfront, he sailed off into the open sea on 25th June. There were no fanfares, and the only farewells were from a few of the locals, who thought him quite mad.

He aimed initially for Cape Clear on the South coast of Ireland, and in spite of a lack of special instruments and a compass giving the wrong readings his navigation was reasonably accurate. Within the first 34 days he survived a number of severe squalls, during which he had to take down both sails and mast and had to stream a sea anchor. He seldom slept at night, ate very little, and had to remain at the helm virtually all the time.

In early August his little craft was struck by a terrible storm when he was about 250 miles west of Cape Clear. Alfred took down the sails and mast as usual, but in huge seas the **Centennial** was tossed about like a cork and eventually broached and capsized. The intrepid sailor was flung into the sea, but he managed to hang onto the boat at the height of the storm; and then, through a superhuman effort, he managed to right it and climb back on board. For many hours, still in a maelstrom of screaming wind, driving rain and breaching seas, he baled furiously; and at last, when the storm abated, he was able to take stock of the situation. Most of his food and water had been lost, and his mast was broken. His sails were badly damaged, and many of his ropes had disappeared. His remaining food was in the forward locker, awash with sea water.

A born survivor, Alfred managed to rig up some sort of a sail, and over the next five days made about 100 miles. He was then sighted by the crew of the brig **Alfredon**, who first thought that the dory was a floating wreck. On approaching it they were surprised to see the sodden, emaciated and bearded figure of Alfred at the helm. They offered to take him aboard the brig, and although he refused he did accept some supplies of bread and water from them before continuing on his way. Over the next few days he was sighted by various other vessels and was always offered help, but he refused anything save food and water. At last he was given an accurate position by the captain of the **Prince Lombardo**, at which time he was 53 miles south of Wexford Head. A couple of days later, through a chance combination of winds and tides, he limped into Abercastle.

In spite of the warm hospitality of the locals and his own poor physical condition Alfred did not wish to hang about, and after receiving some help with repairs to the **Centennial** he was off again, steering a course for Liverpool. He reached his destination on 17th August, unannounced and uncelebrated. He made contact with various relatives in the city, and after some weeks returned home (this time as a passenger on a sailing ship) to Gloucester, Massachusetts. Again his arrival was unannounced; there was no welcoming committee and not even a letter from the President in recognition of his feat. Alfred did not like blowing his own trumpet, and was soon back at work fishing on the Grand Banks.

Date: 1876   *Source: Raggett 1993*

2.5 Love at Ffair Gurig

One fine June day around the year 1330, Cadwgan Ddu of Aberporth decided that he would travel to Newport to attend Ffair Gurig. His daughter Ellen begged to be allowed to go with him, and since she was a strong-willed girl she got her way.   Father and daughter enjoyed themselves at the fair, but for Ellen enjoyment turned to rapture when she caught sight of a tall, dark young man in the crowd. He had a noble bearing, a scar on his face and the look of a man who had seen the world. Their eyes did not meet, but suddenly Ellen was head-over-heels in love.

She made some enquiries about the good-looking stranger, and discovered that his name was Gwilym ap Owen ap Robert ap Eynon Fawr of Coed Cilrhydd, not far from Nevern. Not in the least put off by his long name (on the contrary, it signified good breeding), Ellen made further inquiries, and discovered that the object of her desire was the youngest son of a noble family of the area who had been educated at Oxford and at the English court. Further, it was rumoured that while in France with the King, he had defeated the French King's champion Sir Tristan in personal combat. On hearing this, Ellen's passions were further inflamed, and from that moment on she could not get Gwilym out of her mind.

Soon it was time to return to Aberporth, but on the journey home Ellen was strangely melancholy, and after that, for several days, she could not eat or sleep. Her parents were worried by her love-sickness; but she would say nothing about the identity of her hero. At last she could stand it no longer, and she slipped away from her home and travelled back to Newport. Being a strong willed young lady, she decided on a direct approach. Near Nevern she asked the way to

Coed Cilrhydd, and after passing the old house of Trewern she soon found herself at Gwilym's front door. She did not know what she was going to do next; probably she simply hoped for a sight of her beloved, and hoped that things might develop from there. She knocked, and Ellen was surprised when the door was opened by a woman. It transpired that she was Gwilym's wife, who welcomed her and invited her in. "I have come to seek Gwilym," said Ellen. The wife said that he was away in the woods, hunting. Then, in a flash of inspiration, Ellen said "Madam, I have come to crave a favour." "Favours are not asked of me very often," replied Gwilym's wife. "But you seem to be a lady of good breeding, and I will grant your request if it is in my power."

At this, Ellen explained that she had seen Gwilym at Ffair Gurig and had fallen madly in love with him. Then she said "My request is that I should be allowed to sleep with Gwilym tonight; after that, I give you my word that neither you or he will ever see me again." The wife was flabbergasted, but she could not go back on her word, and she had to agree. Later on Gwilym returned after his day of hunting in the woods. He gave Ellen a warm greeting. Then his wife explained Ellen's mission, and said that she had agreed to the girl's request. Now Gwilym was flabbergasted too. As a man brought up in the courtly tradition he believed in fidelity within marriage; and at first he refused to have anything to do with Ellen. But at last, after pleading from both Ellen and his wife, he consented. So Ellen spent a blissful night in the arms of the heroic Gwilym, while his wife tried to sleep in another room. Then, next morning, Ellen went on her way, never to return. Nine months later she gave birth to a son, whom she christened Gwilym.......

Date: c 1330

Source: Jones p 68

2.6 The Broth of the Broth

A great prince of Dyfed lived in his palace at Narberth. He was renowned for his generosity, and was in the habit of disguising himself as a beggar and walking around his domain to assess the conditions of the people. One day, while disguised, he was attacked by some villains and although many peasants refused to intervene he was rescued by a peasant named Gwynfi. Later, when he had recovered from his injuries, the prince revealed his identity and invited the peasant to his palace, where he was given fine clothes and sat at the prince's side in the great hall. He was then fed on roasted ox and entertained before he returned to his humble abode.

Some days later the prince was surprised by the arrival of a large company of peasants at the entrance to his palace. "Who are you?" he asked. "Why, we are the neighbours of Gwynfi the peasant," they replied. "And we are come to pay homage and to see your generosity for ourselves." "My good friends, come inside," said the prince. So the men came into the hall and in due course were fed, well enough, on a meal of freshly baked bread and oxtail broth. Then, with their stomachs full, they took their leave.

After about a week had passed, an even larger crowd arrived and demanded to speak to the prince. He came out to meet them. "Who are you?" he asked. The reply came: "Why, we are the neighbours of the neighbours of Gwynfi the peasant, and we are come to pay homage and to see your generosity for ourselves." "Ah yes," said the prince. "Come inside and enjoy my hospitality." So the crowd of ragged peasants jostled into the palace, and sat down at the tables, or on the floor, or wherever they could find space. Then the servants of the prince came in and gave each one a goblet of warm water. No food appeared, and the peasants began to complain vociferously. "The prince is a miser and a fraud," they shouted. "We were told of his generosity, but is this the best that he can do for his loyal subjects?"

The prince heard all the noise and came into the hall. "Now, my good people," he said, "you may go on your way. You are the neighbours of the neighbours of Gwynfi the good peasant who rescued me from death, and you have been rightly fed on the broth of the broth of the tail of the ox that I killed in his honour."

Date: c 1600?   *Source: traditional*

2.7   The Wreck of the Treasure Galleon

This tale was told to Francis Jones by an old farm labourer, some time in the early 1930's. It concerns a dreadful episode which followed the rout of the Spanish Armada in 1588. Some of the battered vessels were forced to flee westward and northward, and to follow the coasts of Wales and Scotland in order to find safety. One great treasure galleon, having lost most of its masts and sails in the sea battle, was driven helplessly before the wind around the Pembrokeshire coast, and towards the wild cliffs and skerries of Pwll Deri.

But before the fated vessel hit the rocks the captain ordered that all the gold nuggets, doubloons and other treasures which the ship carried should be placed in a casket which was hurriedly carried to an open boat. With great difficulty the boat was lowered into the surging and foaming sea, and it cast off with a few men on board. In charge was a young Spanish nobleman, who had been given instructions to land safely if possible and to bury the casket in some convenient spot. The casket was chained to his arm. But the open boat was driven inexorably onto the shore to the north of Pwll Deri and dashed to pieces in the waves. The rowers all perished, but the young nobleman survived by some miracle and scrambled to the shore.

By chance the members of one local family had spotted a little lantern in the prow of the open boat, and they were on the shore when it struck the rocks. They could do nothing for the rowers, but managed to pull the nobleman up out of the water, with a broken arm and a cracked skull. The casket was intact, still chained to his arm. Further along the coast the stricken galleon, its captain and all of the crew, perished on the rocks. After the storm the locals reaped a good harvest from the wreck and it is said that for years afterwards fine Spanish furniture, blankets and other items could be seen in the farmhouses around St Nicholas.

The young Spanish nobleman was taken in and looked after, and when he had been restored to health he was allowed to live on Pencaer unmolested. He fell in love, married, and raised a family; and to this day there are people on Pencaer who will tell you that they are descended from a noble foreign family, and that their ancestors owned a castle in Spain.

But what of the casket? That went of course to the family that had rescued our hero, and its contents enable one generation after

The rowers all perished, but the young nobleman survived by some miracle ...

another to buy land and tenements. Eventually they became very wealthy. All we know about them is that, according to the legend, their farm name begins with "Llan". Could it be Llanwnwr, or Llanferran, or Llandruidion, or even Llanwnda .....?

There is one intriguing footnote to this story. There is a wild little cove north of Pwll Deri which is called Pwll Arian (Silver Cove or Treasure Cove). There can be no doubt that this is the very place where the young nobleman and his casket were thrown ashore by the waves of the storm.

Date: 1588   *Source: Francis Jones, Newscuttings, Vol 27, p 80*

PEMBROKESHIRE
FOLK TALES

STRANGE
HAPPENINGS

3.1 The Gold Ring on the Mountain

One of the most poignant stories of recent years relates to the crash of an RAF Coastal Command Liberator aircraft on the Presely uplands during the Second World War. On 19th September 1944 Liberator EV881, part of No 547 Squadron, took off on a routine maritime reconnaissance mission from St Eval in Cornwall. As on many other occasions the mission was to complete an anti-submarine patrol in the western approaches, one small episode in the unrelenting war against the German U-boats which threatened the convoy routes to Milford Haven, Liverpool and other ports.

This particular aircraft was fitted with Leigh Lights, large searchlights mounted under the starboard wing which were used in conjunction with radar to pick up U-boats during night hours. The same aircraft and crew had been on a nine-hour patrol on the night on 17-18 September, and would normally have been rested for three or four days. But on the afternoon of the 19th they were suddenly called up for another flight -- ostensibly for a Leigh Light training exercise, but probably because there had been a sighting of a U-boat off the Pembrokeshire coast. The crew were scrambled and the aircraft took off into the late afternoon sky. It never returned, and next day it transpired that it had crashed into the mountainside not far from Carn Bica, probably in the darkness. Six of the crew were killed, and only three survived. The aircraft was nine miles off track, and its altimeter had been incorrectly set so that the pilot must have assumed they were 600 feet higher and well clear of any high ground.

In 1984, on the 40th anniversary of the fatal crash, a moving ceremony was held on the crash site involving RAF and British Legion representatives, civic dignitaries, and families and friends of the ill-fated bomber crew. Later a permanent memorial plaque was erected on the steep windswept moorland.

In 1990 Mr and Mrs Knight and their family were on holiday in Pembrokeshire, and decided to take a walk in the Presely uplands. They discovered the crash site, and when the children were looking around for traces of debris they spotted some ammunition in the turf. They called their father over, and when he ran his fingers through the grass he saw something sparkling. He picked up a little object, and discovered that it was a signet ring with the initials SWK engraved upon it. It was in perfect condition, except for a slight crack. He reported the find to Dave Pengilly at RAF Brawdy, and he in turn contacted Malcolm Cullen of the Pembrokeshire Aviation Group. They realised that SWK were the initials of Warrant Officer Stan Kearey, the Liberator pilot, who was one of the six crewmen killed. They immediately contacted Mrs Margaret Rumens of Farnham in Surrey -- the pilot's sister -- and informed her of the find. She was naturally very moved, and informed them that Stan's parents had given both she and her brother identical signet rings on the same day. She had worn hers ever since, although after 46 years it had become faded and fragile.

. So it was that on 19th September 1990 Margaret Rumens was presented with her brother's ring by Group Captain Tim Webb of RAF Brawdy, in a short ceremony at the crash site. Margaret vowed that she would always wear her brother's bright gold ring on her finger, next to her own.

Date: 1990   *Source: John Evans, press cuttings*

3.2 Fox Hunt at Freystrop

One cold winter's day, more than a hundred years ago, a fox hunt was in progress in the Freystrop area. It so happened that the fox led the hunt into the village churchyard. There was pandemonium, with horses and hounds milling about all over the place. The horsemen rushed about madly in all directions. The Master of the Hunt tried to keep a sense of decorum by preventing the riders from entering the cemetery, but some of them did so anyway, and the hounds were not so easy to control. In a yapping and baying frenzy they hunted everywhere around the graves, in the overgrown corners, and among the shrubs and trees, with some of the huntsmen on foot also trying to flush out the fox.

The church rector, who was out for a walk in the crisp frosty air, observed the proceedings with some amusement and not a little concern. In spite of searching high and low the Hunt could find no trace of the fox, and in the end the Master simply had to call off the hounds and set off elsewhere in the hope of picking up another scent. When the coast was clear the rector was amazed to see the fox descend to the ground from the branches of a large and spreading yew tree, where it had been hiding quietly. He went to investigate how the fox had managed to climb the tree, and found that it had jumped up from an old and forgotten tombstone which was more or less buried in the undergrowth. He cleared away the vegetation and eventually was able to read the inscription. It read as follows:

"In memory of Joseph Williams, a brave and honest huntsman who died suddenly at Pill Earth after a terrible fox chase, October 26th 1786, aged 32 years."

Date: c 1880   *Source: newspaper cutting*

The horsemen rushed about madly in all directions.

3.3 The Hound of the Scourfields

One of the strangest stories of the Pembrokeshire gentry is set in the little hamlet of New Moat, in the Presely foothills. Here there was once a thriving township, established by the Norman colonists close to the "high tide mark" of their settlement in Pembrokeshire. There was a castle mound surmounted by a timber structure, a little fortified settlement with burgage plots, a church and a manor.

Sir Fulk Scourfield was granted the manor of New Moat by King Edward I, and the family remained powerful in the area until the 1800s. The family mansion is long since lost in the woods, but the church with its tall battlemented "Englishry" tower contains the last traces of the Scourfields. There are several examples of the Scourfield coat of arms, the most interesting feature of which is a pack of racing greyhounds. According to legend, the family was obsessed with the sport of hunting with dogs, and also with dog racing accompanied by sizeable wagers. On one occasion there were two contending heirs for the Scourfield estate, and they decided to settle the inheritance by means of a greyhound race. The winner took all, and understandably developed a deep affection for the hound that had brought him his good fortune.

There is a strange footnote to this tale. In the Scourfield family vault beneath the church there is a row of damp dark lead coffins which contain the remains of six of the Scourfield squires. The coffins were once draped with funeral hangings, velvets and rich tapestries on wooden frames, and they are raised off the floor on blocks to allow the circulation of air and to prevent damage by flood-waters. The coffins are interesting enough, but on the floor next to the tomb of one William Scourfield, who died in 1622, is a pathetic little pile of animal bones. On closer examination they are seen to be the bones of a whippet or small greyhound, curled up as if fast asleep at his master's feet. It was believed by the old people of New Moat that this was the original greyhound that secured the estate for its master; and that when he died the dog would not leave him, but curled up at the side of the coffin in the vault, where at last it died of a broken heart.

Date: c 1622   *Source: Brinton and Worsley p 152; Miles p 53*

3.4 The Society of Sea Serjeants

In these days of Parliamentary sleaze and concern about the "behind the scenes" operation of free-masonry in political life, it is worth reminding ourselves that Pembrokeshire has a sound history of secret societies. One of the strangest was the Society of Sea Serjeants which operated in the county between 1726 and 1762.

Its origins lay in the sympathies of most of the Pembrokeshire gentry for the Tory party and the Jacobite cause. In the closing years of the seventeenth century most of the gentry hoped for the return of James II, and at the time of the Jacobite rising of 1715 many of them broke up "loyalist" meetings by sending in their retainers and hired thugs to beat up the opposition. Following the failure of the rising, Jacobite sympathies lingered on, and led to the formation of the Society of Sea Serjeants in 1726. It was a highly secretive club which existed largely to influence the course of Pembrokeshire elections.

The Society had 25 members, including a president, secretary, examiner and two stewards. Much of their work was behind the scenes and was unrecorded, but once a year they held a week-long anniversary meeting in one of the Pembrokeshire sea-side towns. On these occasions the members were subject to strict discipline, and they had to wear the proper uniform and a badge consisting of a silver star with a dolphin figure in the centre. Presumably the identities of the members were well known to other influential people in the county.

The two most powerful families in Pembrokeshire were the Owens of Orielton and the Philippses of Picton Castle. The Sea Serjeants were devoted to the strengthening of the Philipps cause and the downfall of the Owens family. Their most blatant coup occurred in July 1760 when no less than 28 Sea Serjeants past and present were created burgesses of the borough of Haverfordwest on the pretext that "they have deserved well of this Corporation." This had the effect of creating an electoral stranglehold on the county town and ensuring the election of a powerful group of country gentlemen who thereafter sat in the House of Commons.

After 1760 the new king, George III, won over the Jacobite families and the secret society of Sea Serjeants, with no more need for political wheeling and dealing behind the scenes, dissolved themselves in 1762. Or did they........?

Date: 1762   *Source: Miles p 144*

3.5 Sir John and the Cargo of Salt

In Elizabethan times piracy and smuggling were looked upon by many people as perfectly acceptable activities. Pembrokeshire, with its long and difficult coastline, was an ideal place for smugglers, especially since it was a long way from London. Another factor which encouraged lawlessness was the blatant corruption within the Excise Service; many of the customs officers were "bent", and wealthy merchants and even magistrates were themselves involved in the purchase and sale of goods obtained by pirates and smugglers.

One day in the year 1570 a pirate named Edward Herberde was operating off the Pembrokeshire coast when he happened upon a trading vessel laden with a cargo of salt. The ship was owned and sailed by a Dutchman named Peter Muncke. Herberde sailed alongside and demanded -- and obtained -- immediate surrender. After taking the ship Herberde trussed up the captain and his sailors, put a prize crew on board, and instructed his men to sail on in the company of his own ship. However, the two vessels were separated in a storm, and with their master out of sight, the prize crew decided to take the vessel into Milford Haven themselves. There they planned to dispose of the valuable cargo of salt and to pocket the proceeds before disappearing out into the emptiness of the Bristol Channel. They sailed the vessel into Pembroke and anchored under the shadow of the castle. The two ringleaders made it clear to the Dutch captain that they expected his cooperation; if they did not get it, both he and his captive crew members would have their throats slit. Then they went into town with the frightened captain, to try and find a buyer for the salt.

It happened to be market day, and the Mayor of Pembroke noticed the strange trio approaching the town cross. He became suspicious, and decided that the best-dressed of the men (the captain) looked frightened and was probably acting under duress. When the two conspirators had their backs turned, the Mayor managed to exchange a few words with the captain, who confirmed that both he and his ship were prisoners of pirates from Herberde's gang. The Mayor then declared that he knew a buyer for the whole cargo -- Sir John Perrott of Carew. He suggested that Peter Muncke and one of the conspirators should accompany him to Carew Castle, where he would introduce them to Sir John. So off they went while the other pirate returned to the ship. As soon as they reached Carew the

Mayor arranged for the pirate to be seized, and with the cooperation of Sir John (who was an old hand at dealing with stolen cargoes) a plan was quickly hatched for the recovery of both ship and cargo.

That evening, as a damp and quiet dusk descended over the Pembroke River, two longboats pushed off from the quay. In the first boat was Peter Muncke, a Captain Hinde who was in the service of Sir John, and another man named Rice Thomas. In the second boat were Sir John and twelve of his men. As the longboats drew alongside his stolen ship, Peter Muncke climbed on board and shouted to his captured crew, urging them to turn on their captors. This was none too easy for them since they were all roped up. But they made lots of noise, and at the same time the well-armed men from Sir John's boat climbed up the ship's side, and after a short sharp battle overwhelmed the pirate prize crew. Three or four of them escaped, and managed to get into a small boat which they rowed off towards the Haven. The majority, battered and bruised, were imprisoned.

Peter Muncke released his own crew members from the cabin where they were bound, and assumed with great relief that he would now be free to resume possession of his ship and cargo. Life was not so simple, for Sir John now declared the ship and cargo to be booty. He claimed (and got) half the cargo as a reward for his part in the affair. The Town Mayor was rewarded with five tons of salt. John Vaughan, the merchant who was the intended customer for the salt in the first place, received no salt but was given part-ownership of the ship and her tackle. One Richard Vaughan was also given part-ownership by virtue of the fact that he was Deputy Vice Admiral of South Wales. The Dutchman, deprived of his ship, was paid off with the rest of the salt and was "encouraged" to leave post haste.

Once the poor fellow had disappeared from the scene, a trial was organized at Haverfordwest Assizes; but when it became clear that Muncke was nowhere to be found the case against the incompetent pirates collapsed, and the Judge was obliged to set them free. The circumstances surrounding the affair were thus never properly examined in court, which suited all concerned.

In all probability the pirates resumed their chosen careers off the Pembrokeshire coast, although it would hardly have been in the employ of Edward Herberde. We may safely assume that the pirate leader was not at all amused by the "theft" of his prize vessel and the loss of the cargo of salt by his own hand-picked prize crew..........

Date: c 1570   *Source: Carradice p 76*

3.6 Leekie Porridge and the Silver Buckles

The Scottish - American pirate John Paul Jones was well known in Pembrokeshire waters, and there are a number of local tales about his activities in the period 1785 - 1790. He was seen particularly frequently in the Tenby area, and it was well known that he came ashore frequently on Caldey Island to take on water supplies. He had various local accomplices including one Leekie Porridge, who may have been the same man referred to in the story of Tenby and the Beggar's Curse (Vol 1, story 7.18).

After the death of the pirate captain (and his reputed burial on Caldey island) Leekie Porridge returned home to Tenby and became a respectable pilot, helping visiting ship's captains to steer clear of the rocks and sandbanks around Tenby and Caldey Island. Many of the locals must have known about Leekie's piratical past, but there was always a sneaking admiration for the pirates who ran rings around the Excise Men, and he was never handed over to the authorities.

But then one day, as Leekie went aboard a cargo ship out in the bay, the captain recognized him as one of John Paul Jones' men, having been robbed by the pirate crew at the peak of the pirate captain's infamous career. The captain kept quiet until his ship was safely into Tenby Harbour on the high tide, and then he reported him to the magistrates. Leekie was duly arrested, and when the case came before the court, the visiting captain produced convincing evidence as to Leekie's murky past. The most spectacular part of the captain's case was that Leekie had upon his shoes a fine pair of silver buckles which Leekie had stolen from him when his vessel had been plundered. The magistrates were convinced, and Leekie was duly convicted. He was sentenced to be put on board a British man-of-war as a quarter-master, from which position he had previously deserted in order to join the pirate captain.

Leekie duly served out his time in the British Navy until peace was proclaimed following the defeat of Napoleon, and he then returned to live out the rest of his days in Tenby.

Date: c 1795   *Source: Bielski, 1979, p 8*

3.7 Incident at Freshwater East

One dark winter's evening Lord Cawdor and his family were sitting down to their evening meal in the grest dining room of Stackpole Court. Like many such meals, it was a mellow candle-lit occasion, and the conversation ranged across politics, cattle prices, poetry and music. Suddenly the butler came in and said: "Excuse me, my lord, but George Beynon of Trewent wishes to speak with you. He says it is most urgent."

"Show him in. Show him in," said Lord Cawdor. George Beynon was ushered into the dining room, mud-splattered and ruddy-faced. "My lord, there is dirty work afoot," he said. "I have rode directly from Freshwater East. There is a ship in the bay, and in the moonlight I seen at least ten men comin' ashore with heavy casks. Smugglers, I do believe. They're awaitin' for their confederates to come with a horse an' cart, unless I'm very much mistook."

"Well done, Beynon!" exclaimed Lord Cawdor, leaping to his feet. "You must be right. The moon is almost full and the night is calm -- perfect weather for landing contraband. Casks of Spanish wine, I shouldn't be surprised. And not a single Excise Man between Manorbier and Bosherston. Let us see what we can do."

And with that he left his half-eaten meal, gave his apologies to his family, and rushed out. He called his stable-lad to saddle up his best horse and sent messages to three of his nearest neighbours asking them to join him on the road to Freshwater East with all possible haste. When all four of the gallant gentlemen were together they galloped off into the night in a thunder of hooves and with their cloaks streaming behind them in the cold dank air.

Soon they were on the hill leading down to the sandy bay. Ahead of them they could see a ketch close inshore with sails furled, and a small group of men standing alongside a pile of casks on the beach. They rushed on, determined to confront the villains. However, at the sound of the horses' hooves the three smugglers on the beach became convinced that a large posse was after them, and ran off to hide amid the blackthorn thickets and sand dunes at the head of the beach. Lord Cawdor and his three worthy friends were now in possession of the pile of casks of red wine, but they were too heavy to move. They held a conference on what to do next, but felt no great sense of urgency since they were convinced that the smugglers would now take up their anchor, set sail and depart.

To the great disquiet of the small forces of law and order, it became obvious that the smugglers were not prepared to lose their precious cargo without a fight. On realising that there were only four men in the posse, the ship's captain immediately dispatched two boat-loads of villains. As soon as they landed on the shore it transpired that they were armed with pokers, bludgeons, knives and axes, and at this point the redoubtable Lord Cawdor realised that he and his friends were in deep trouble. He was normally a man who planned things in meticulous detail, but on this occasion he and his neighbours had rushed off to intercept the smugglers in such greast haste that they had quite forgotten to arm themselves.

They were defenceless against the weapons of the smugglers, and although they put up a stiff fight all four of them were badly injured before the villains loaded the casks back onto the rowing boats and ferried them to the ketch. Then, leaving their victims battered and bruised on the beach, the smugglers set sail and left the bay, no doubt to find another customer for their contraband elsewhere.

Lord Cawdor took some time to recover from the injuries received during the affray, but as a military officer of some renown his pride was considerably more bruised than his body.

Date: c 1799   *Source: Carradice p 78*

3.8 The Legend of Bedd Morris

Bedd Morris (or Morus) is a massive standing stone located on the misty upland ridge of Carningli and Dinas Mountain, at the highest point on the road between Newport and Pontfaen. According to some, it is a Bronze Age boundary marker, or a waymark, or a fertility symbol, or a memorial to some ancient chieftain. But these theories are not at all romantic, and there are two local legends which help to explain the name, which means "the grave of Morris."

According to one legend, Morris was a highwayman who terrorised the old road across the mountain and who relieved many travellers of their possessions. He lived in a cave up among the crags on the mountain top, and his only friend was a little white dog. But at last the locals organized a posse and attacked his cave. He was caught, together with the dog. The dog's throat was cut and he was hanged by the roadside on a gallows erected for this purpose. As his corpse hung there on its taut rope, swinging grotesquely in the constant wind that buffets the mountain, the authorities determined to erect a stone which would act as a reminder to following generations that highway robbery does not pay.

More romantic, but equally sad, is the legend of a young man called Morris who lived in Newport hundreds of years ago. He was desperately in love with the fair maid of Pontfaen, and she with him. But her father the squire considered Morris to be beneath her station and would not give consent for the marriage. Instead he arranged a marriage with another young man, in spite of the tearful entreaties of his daughter. So the young people decided, secretly, to resolve the issue themselves. Morris challenged his rival to a duel, and they met up on the mountain, at the highest point on the road, to fight to the death. Morris was killed in the duel, and he was buried where the stone now stands. And as in all these sad and romantic tales, the daughter took to her bed, shocked by the horror of it all, and eventually died of a broken heart.............

Now the stone is used as a boundary marker between the parishes of Newport and Llanychlwydog. It bears the initials of Thomas Davies Lloyd, who was Lord of Cemais in the mid-1800s and who was responsible for the conversion of part of the ruined Newport Castle into a Victorian mansion. The stone is also on the route of the annual "beating of the bounds" perambulation by aldermen, burgesses, townspeople and visitors, which takes place in August each year. The ceremony, which may well be several centuries old, was designed originally to check the parish boundaries and to ensure that there was no encroachment upon them. Nowadays the riders and walkers do not follow the whole of the boundary around the parish, but Bedd Morris is a key location on the route because it is here that small boys are beaten (very gently indeed) so that they will remember exactly where the boundary runs.

Date: c 1500?   *Source: word of mouth; Miles 1995 p 54*

3.9 The Last Wreckers at Pendine

The bleak and lonely coast around Marros and Pendine had, in the bad old days, a reputation for wrecking and smuggling. The vast open expanse of Pendine Sands was particularly dangerous for shipping especially when an onshore gale was screaming in from the south or south-east; when hundreds of sailing ships plied their trade along this coast some casualties were guaranteed every winter. It used to be said that most of the houses of Pendine were made of shipwreck timber. The locals had a reputation for the merciless manner in which they plundered wrecked vessels, and naturally enough there were frequent tales of false lights and organized wrecking activities on the part of certain families.

The last of the Pendine wrecks to be stripped by the locals was the **Treviga,** cast up at Morfabychan on the Marros side of Ragwen Point. She was a Russian schooner from Riga, en route from Trinidad to Cardiff with a cargo of pitch. She was caught in a gale and the skipper, Captain Jacobson, decided to seek shelter inside Caldey Island. Jack Childs, a Saundersfoot pilot, went out the the schooner and offered to take her in to the safety of Tenby Harbour; but the skipper declined to pay the dues and decided to ride out the storm as best he could. In the event, the schooner dragged her anchor during the night and was driven across the bay out of control. The alarm was raised, and the Tenby lifeboat managed to take off the skipper, his wife and the crew of seven before the vessel was driven onto the maelstrom of Morfabychan beach.

According to legend, when the skipper travelled from Tenby to Morfabychan a couple of days later to see what could be salvaged from the wreck, he could see from the clifftop that there was virtually nothing left. Lumps of pitch and ship's timbers lay around on the sands and on the rocks, but virtually all of the sails, ropes, and metal fittings, as well as the cabin and bridge contents, had disappeared. On his way down the hill to examine the wreck, the captain passed a local woman coming up, looking very elegant in his wife's fur coat.

Date: 1923   *Source: Roscoe Howells 1978 p 121*

3.10 Tragedy at Hangstone Davy

Between Broadway and Portfield Gate, lost in the hedge at the side of the road, there is an old standing stone called Hangstone Davy. It is only 4 ft high, but it is deeply buried in the ground, and it has probably been there since the Bronze Age. There is an old legend associated with its name. Long ago the land hereabouts used to be unenclosed common land, and many local farmers had grazing rights which they guarded jealously.

Now it happened one dark night that a sheep-stealer named Davy or Dafydd arrived, and when nobody was looking he grabbed a fine fat ram. He managed to rope up its legs, and once it was immobilised he slung it up onto his shoulders, with two feet by his right ear and two by his left ear, and the rope held firmly in his hands across his chest. But the beast put up quite a struggle, and Davy decided that he needed to get a better hold on it. The old standing stone was nearby, and a convenient height, so he leaned back against it and let the ram down onto the top of it. Strange to relate, the ram struggled again and slipped down the back of the stone while Davy was still at the front. With the ram now on one side of the stone and Davy on the other, the poor man let go of the rope, which immediately tightened across his neck and throttled him.

When they found him next day he was dead as a dodo, still pinned to the rock by the rope across his neck. The ram was still alive and still struggling, and was greatly relieved to be released. And since that day the stone has been called "Hangstone Davy" by the locals.

Date: 1500?   *Source: Francis Green News Cuttings 12, p 91*

3.11 The Wrecking of the St David's Bell

There are many legends associated with church bells, and there are a number which relate to the bells of St David's Cathedral. Originally the tower was quite low, so as to remain out of sight of the Viking pirates who sailed up and down the coast. In this first squat tower there were eight bells; later, when the second and third storeys were added, the number of bells may have been reduced each time, so that by 1690 there were only five. In the early part of the eighteenth century the cathedral was in a terrible state, having suffered from both neglect and deliberate destruction since the time of Bishop Barlow around 1540. Much more damage was done by Parliamentary troops during the Civil War. In 1748 there were such concerns about the weight of the bells and the deteriorating fabric of the tower that all but one were taken down. Later they were re-located in the restored tower which forms part of the gate-house at the lower end of the Pobbles.

The original bells were cast in Bishop Gower's time (1328 - 1347), and the heaviest of them weighed more than a tonne. When it was taken down for re-casting in 1748 it was so difficult to handle that the tower was cracked and there were grave concerns that it might collapse. Suspicious local people believed that the bell, having caused so much trouble, was determined not to leave St David's. When it was shipped out of the little "cathedral port" of Porthclais a great storm blew up, and the vessel carrying it was shipwrecked. Naturally enough, the lost bell can still be heard tolling beneath the surface when storm waves are rolling up from the south.

Date: 1748   *Source: word of mouth*

3.12 The Last Pembrokeshire Smuggler

One of the last authenticated episodes of spirits smuggling occurred in the lonely bay of Swanlake in the summer of 1825. The farmer there was an acquaintance of a Mr Jenkins of Pembroke, who had something of a reputation for the "unofficial" importation of various cargoes from abroad. Jenkins was planning for the landing of a large cargo of contraband spirits on Swanlake beach, and he asked the farmer and his wife (whose names were Lewis and Mary) if the cargo could be temporarily stored in the cellar under their kitchen while arrangements were made for the final disposal of the barrels to a network of customers. The couple agreed, assuming that they would at least get a barrel of rum out of the deal.

However, the couple were not well off, and it was well known that sizeable rewards were being offered by the Customs Officers for the apprehension of smugglers and illicit cargoes. They calculated that they could obtain more than £200 if they betrayed Jenkins and his accomplices. So it was that the cargo was landed one moonlit Thursday night and safely packed away in the farmhouse cellar.

On the following Saturday a housewife in Manorbier met Mary hurrying along the road towards Tenby. She was hot and bothered, and carried her small daughter in her arms. "Where art tha goin', Mary?" she asked. "Tha looks very bothered, and with such a load as well."

"Oh, I'll tell just thee," replied Mary. "Lewis and me has been left in charge of a cargo of smuggled spirits for that Mr Jenkins of Pembroke. And we has agreed to inform, and get the reward, and that, as tha can well imagine, would be a great thing for the likes of us. So farewell now, I cannot stay any longer." And off she rushed towards Tenby.

The housewife happened to be an old employee of Mr Jenkins, and was still very loyal to him, so she put her bonnet on and rushed off to his house in Pembroke. She found him in the garden and asked if he had indeed landed a cargo of spirits in Swanlake on Thursday night. He looked at her suspiciously and said "What if I have?" "Well sir," replied the flushed housewife, "if tha has, lose no time. For Mary is gone to Tenby to inform the Custom House officers of it, and they will be after you within the hour."

Mr Jenkins sprang into action. Within 15 minutes he had eight men who stole out of Pembroke singly so as not to attract attention. Some went over Monkton Bridge and over the common, and others

went through the town. They all met at Swanlake, having collected on the way another forty men to help in the task of clearing the farmhouse cellar. Lewis the farmer was brushed aside and showered with curses, and in no time at all the barrels of spirits were removed. Some were stored at Sunny Hill, and others in various safe places through the countryside. By the time Mary returned from Tenby on Saturday night there was no sign either of the frantic activity or the contraband cargo.

The Customs men arrived at the farm first thing on Monday morning (they were not very quick in those days, and did not like working on weekends). Mary of course knew that the contraband had gone, but she led the officers to the cellar and feigned surprise when it transpired that it was quite empty. The men returned to Tenby in a state of high dudgeon.

After that, Mary and Lewis were not particularly popular with the smuggling and drinking classes in the neighbourhood. The spirits were all disposed of safely, but Mr Jenkins and his accomplices had had a very close shave, and thereafter turned to more legal pursuits. Mr Jenkins had a family of fourteen children and a previous conviction for smuggling; if he had been caught during or after the Swanlake incident, he might well have been transported to the penal colonies.

Date: 1825   *Source: Mason, 1858; Bielski p 13*

3.13 The Gold Hoard of Y Cwrt

Court Farm (Y Cwrt) lies not far from Llanychaer on the flank of the Gwaun Valley. In the eighteenth and nineteenth centuries it was the home of the Gwynne family, who were much respected squires and farmers This tale was told to Francis Jones by an old lady of 86; and it probably relates to the mid-1800s.

According to local tradition the Gwynne family kept all their wealth in the form of gold sovereigns, and as they prospered they accumulated so many that they could no longer be stored in stockings or drawers. Coins used to lie about all over the place, but most of them were kept in a large sieve in an old oak coffer in the hall of the mansion. It was common knowledge that there were piles of gold sovereigns in the house; but the local people were totally honest, and since the family was well known for its generosity and good living, its members appeared to have no enemies. In any case, in those days nobody thought there could be burglars or villains in Cwm Gwaun. The family kept open house, and people wandered in and out at will.

One year the time came for the squire of Cwrt to pay his taxes. So he opened up the coffer, looked into the sieve and was flabbergasted to find that but a handful of coins remained. Someone, somehow, had taken a large fortune of gold coins from the coffer. Could the thief have been a neighbour, or a tradesman, or a visitor from far away, or even a family servant?   The mysterious disappearance of the fortune was never solved, but the family was rocked back on its heels by the loss and barely survived the years following the theft.

So it was that a local proverb arose in the Gwaun Valley. Whenever a householder or farmer bought some land or property, the locals would smile and say (in Welsh) "There is the gold of Cwrt showing itself."

Date: c 1855   *Source: Francis Jones, Newscuttings Vol 27, p 65*

3.14   The Coins of Llangwarren

About 1819 the old mansion at Llangwarren, not far from Letterston, was undergoing extensive alterations. In the course of the work a group of labourers and a foreman were demolishing an old wall that had a window and a window seat in it. The window was taken out, and a ladder placed against the sill from the outside so that the rest of the wall could be lowered, stone by stone, down to the level of the ground outside. William, the foreman, went up the ladder and started to move the stones, but suddenly he stopped and said "Time for breakfast now, lads. We are a little late."   The workmen were surprised by this, for as he came down the ladder they looked at their watches and realised that they were in fact a little early. They did not complain, since they were hungry and in need of their breakfast so off they trooped to their little shed, where they settled down to their bread and cheese.

After a while they realised that William was not with them, so one of them went back to the big house and to the spot where they had been working. William was nowhere to be seen. The man called his colleagues and when one of their number climbed up the ladder he saw, in the partly demolished window seat beneath the window space, a broken earthenware vessel. On the ground at the foot of the ladder there was a scatter of silver coins, clearly dropped by somebody in a hurry. They put them in a bag. They were from the reigns of James I, Charles I and Louis XIV, and some had been cut in two to be used as half-pieces. The men destroyed the remains of the urn, and told nobody. But when their day's work had come to an end, they were happy enough to share out the coins among themselves.

Nothing further was heard of William for many years. He seemed to have vanished completely, and was never again seen in the Letterston area.   But then, many years afterwards, one of the workmen happened to be in Haverfordwest and called in at one of the more refined inns for a tankard of ale. He was served by a jovial, corpulent and prosperous landlord and recognized him immediately. Nothing was said, but it was clear that the old foreman had managed to set himself up in some style, helped no doubt by a small fortune in ready cash.

Date: 1819   *Source: Francis Jones, Newscuttings Vol 27, p 36*

3.15 Duel at Withybush

One of the lesser-known episodes in the life of General Sir Thomas Picton (see story 2.2 above) was a duel with the agricultural surveyor Charles Hassall, probably in the year 1813. Sir Thomas had an extensive estate at Poyston, near Rudbaxton and Withybush, and when he was resting between wars he loved nothing more than to return to his home territory and to indulge in the normal country pursuits of the landed gentry – in particular hunting, shooting and fishing. It so happened that he went to a ball in Haverfordwest, possibly intent upon finding a wife, but while he was there he got into a heated argument with Charles Hassall, who was renowned for his hot temper. Hassall challenged Sir Thomas to a duel, and the great man had to accept.

On the appointed day, probably at dawn, the men met with their attendants in the old quarry at Withybush, armed with pistols. The duel commenced. The General missed his adversary completely, but was himself wounded when the ball from Hassall's gun gave him a flesh wound on the side of his neck. He was pretty tough, and soon recovered; but the locals surmised that, what with the Peninsular War and assorted other campaigns, and now a very close shave in this duel, he had used up most if not all of his nine lives.

And so it proved. A couple of years later, when he was called once again into action against Napoleon, he had a premonition that he would not return. At the beginning of June he said an emotional farewell to the haymakers on his estate as they were at work in the meadows, and three weeks later he died heroically on the battlefield at Waterloo.

Date: 1813   *Source: Francis Green Cuttings vol 12, p 118*

PEMBROKESHIRE
FOLK TALES

FAIRY
TALES

4.1 Strange Arrival at Cardigan

Once upon a time a young man called Guto was out for a walk in the waterfall country of the vale of Neath. For a moment he rested near one of the Clungwyn Falls on the River Mellte, and rejoiced in the cool spray on his face. Suddenly the cascading froth and foam of the waterfall took on the shape and sound of a magnificent snow-white stallion, and as Guto watched in astonishment the beast whinnied and came towards him. It nuzzled up to him as if inviting him to jump onto its back, and he found it impossible to resist.

No sooner had the young man mounted the horse than it was away! It flared its nostrils, tossed its head, and galloped like the wild wind through the countryside. Poor Guto held on for dear life as the water horse sped on across hedges and fields, farms and villages; it felt as if it was flying, for it did not stumble once in spite of the many obstacles in its course. As the minutes passed the young man's initial sense of exhilaration turned to fright as the countryside flashed below him. And then, after what seemed no longer than five minutes, the magic stallion descended into a field and came to a standstill. Guto dismounted, thoroughly shaken by the experience, and as he did so the stallion disappeared in a flash of lightning.

Guto had no idea where he was, but the sea was nearby and he called at a fisherman's cottage and asked where he was. He was relieved to discover that the inhabitants spoke Welsh, and they told him that he was not far from Cardigan town. He explained that he had been carried through the air by a strange white stallion all the way from the Vale of Neath, and the fisherman looked not at all surprised. "Duw Duw," he said. "There's lucky you are. That was the *ceffyl dwr* right enough. Mostly those who ride on its back are taken out to sea and are never seen again. So, Guto bach, you can count your lucky stars."

It took Guto three days to walk home from Cardigan, and when he explained his absence to his family and friends they rolled their eyes, nudged each other, and roared with laughter. Guto was most offended at this response. "Oh ye of little faith!" he exclaimed. "That's my story, and I'm sticking to it." And after that he never dared again to walk all by himself around the cascading waterfalls of Pont Nedd Fechan.

Date: c 1800?   *Source: Evans & Willis p 24*

4.2 The Fairies at Pentre Ifan

There is a very old tradition that fairies can be seen on moonlit nights dancing around the old cromlech at Pentre Ifan. An old lady from the Cardigan area told Evans Wentz that her mother had seen the fairies at Pentre Ifan. They looked like little children dressed in soldier's clothes, and with red caps on their heads.

There is a story of two old friends in Cardigan who were discussing the theory that fairies had actually built Pentre Ifan back in the good old days when the *tylwyth teg* were the main inhabitants of the area. Mr Jones argued that no human beings could have lifted up the massive capstone, and declared that the job must have been done by either Merlin the Wizard, or the fairies.

"No, no!" said Mr O'Connor (who happened to be Irish). "It is well known, to be sure, that before the Welsh came here, the Irish were in this old county of Pembrokeshire. They were a blessed folk, and they learnt how to be navvies by building things like this every day of the week. To get the capstone up, all they needed was an English foreman and a thousand men all pulling the same way."

"There's rubbish you are talking," retorted Mr Jones. "Now then, where on earth would you find a thousand Irishmen pulling the same way? The truth of the matter is, man, that a Welsh tribe, in a wonderful feat of organization, built Pentre Ifan in a couple of weeks to hold the remains of an old chieftain, God bless his soul."

"Impossible!" said Mr O'Connor. "If it was a Welsh tribe that tried to build it, they would have had a hundred committees, and they would still be trying to sort out the agenda."

Mr Jones had to agree, and so they came to the mutual conclusion that the fairies had probably done the job after all.

Date: 1990   *Source: Wentz, p 155; word of mouth*

4.3 The Wandering Cobbler of Nolton

This story was written down by Charles Wilkins in 1879. In his text he went to great lengths to disguise the location and the key personalities, but the tale can only be set in the area around Nolton.

John Morgan Thomas was a cobbler in Nolton village. He was a clever and hard-working man who made and repaired clogs and boots for the farmers and miners who lived along the coast of St Bride's Bay between Little Haven and Newgale. There was plenty of work to be had, especially from the miners who worked in tough conditions in the many small mines and drifts which were opening up at the time. Every day around lunch-time John would settle down either in "The Ship" or in one of the other inns (which were numerous) down on the haven where the coal ships were loaded, or in the village a little further inland. He always explained to his wife that it was the fairies or *tylwyth teg* who led him astray from his work-bench, and that there were so many of them that he could never resist their cajoling and pulling and pestering and pinching. He described the fairies as very small in stature, quick in their movements, excitable and mischievous. They spoke in high-pitched voices and laughed and chatted incessantly. John said that although they were a terrible nuisance, he was actually quite fond of them.

One day there was a scandal in the village when a very sombre and proper funeral procession was making its way along the sea-shore road. Everybody was dressed up to the nines, the men in their shiny black boots, dark suits and stiff collars, and the ladies in their big hats and black Sunday dresses. All of a sudden John rushed down the hill from the village and joined the procession, dressed in his leather apron and working clothes, with wild hair flying in all directions in the wind, and making a frightful noise. Of course they all said afterwards that it was most embarrassing, and that he was rolling drunk and should be arrested for such behaviour; but John insisted that he had been pushed into the procession by the fairies that only he could see.

One day John set off very early with a pair of shiny new boots which he had to deliver to a farmer up in the mountains around Wolfscastle and Treffgarne. He should have been back by nightfall, but when he had not returned his wife began to worry, and she passed a sleepless night waiting up for him in the kitchen. Next day there was no sign of him either, and so Mrs John Morgan Thomas walked around the village and the haven, and up and down to all the coal-mines and local farms, to see if anybody had caught sight of him. Nobody had any news. She began to fear that he might have fallen into one of the old bell-pits used by the miners in the old days, and so a search was mounted by a group of neighbours. Still there was no trace of him. Another night passed.

Next morning the cobbler's wife and a couple of friends walked all the way to the farm near Treffgarne which John was due to have visited. The farmer said that he had arrived, delivered the boots, taken a nice spot of dinner and then set off for home. He emphasised that he had had hardly anything to drink, and that he was stone cold sober when he left through the front door. The deputation returned to Nolton, and when news came that further searches had also drawn a blank, Mrs John Morgan Thomas at last decided that her husband must have fallen down an old mine shaft and been killed. Or maybe all this talk of fairies had been true? Maybe they had finally taken him away to *Gwlad y Tylwyth Teg*, the fairyland where captives could spend their lives in feasting and all manner of wonderful pleasures?

The poor lady was sobbing in the corner of her kitchen, consoled by a couple of friends, when there was a knock on the door. It was the constable from Little Haven, with John Morgan Thomas in tow. He explained that he had found him, smelling of whisky and somewhat the worse for wear, at the roadside in Broad Haven, and had locked him up in his little cell so that he could sleep off his alcoholic stupour in warm and comfortable conditions. Where he had been the first night he could not say. When the constable and the friends had left, John explained his adventures in great detail to his wife, explaining that the fairies had accosted him by the roadside on his way home from Treffgarne and had led him astray over fields and along strange lanes and pathways until he had fallen into a ditch. He had climbed out, only to be pestered by them again and again until he had taken refuge in an old colliery hut, where he had spent the night. And so the story went on........

Until his dying day John the cobbler maintained that his story was absolutely true. His wife was not at all certain, however, for all the money he had been paid for the new boots by the Treffgarne farmer had disappeared, and John had always told her that the fairies never ever stole money from those whom they pestered.

Date: c 1830   *Source: Wilkins p 95*

4.4 Fairies at Caerfarchell

In the St David's district around 1830 children were warned to be careful when walking in the fields lest they strayed into one of "Bendith y Mammau's Rings." It was said that if one stepped inside a fairy ring of this sort one would have to sing and dance for a year and a day with the *Tylwyth Teg* or fairies. What is more, while one was with the fairies one would lose all track of time. Precisely at the end of the magical period someone had to come and pull out the enchanted person, or else they would have to stay there, singing and dancing, for ever.

One day a woman who lived near Caerfarchell was baking bread in her kitchen when she heard the sound of beautiful music, carried in fragments on the sweet breath of the wind. She was immediately enchanted, and after putting her loaf "on the plank" she ran into the meadow behind the house to find out who the musicians were. She ran straight into a mushroom circle and was swept up into the frenzy of singing and dancing by the fairies who inhabited it. And there she remained for a year and a day.

The woman's husband, daughter and friends realised what had happened, and they noted the precise position of the Bendith y Mammau's Ring in the meadow. At the appointed time in the following year they came to the rescue, and cautiously approached the enchanted circle. They saw her inside, singing with gay abandon and swirling and weaving in the fairy dance. At last, when she danced near the edge of the circle they made a human chain, and one of them grabbed hold of her and dragged her out. She collapsed on the ground, quite exhausted, but at last she came to herself again. She immediately turned to her daughter and asked: "Mary, have you turned the loaf?"

Date: c 1830   *Source: Francis Green Newscuttings, Vol 11 p 151*

4.5 The Fairy King and Queen

There was once a belief in the eastern parts of Pembrokeshire that the fairies had a king and a queen. The *tylwyth teg* themselves were as small in stature as dwarves. They always wore white clothes. Often they would dance at night within their magic circles in green fields. Most of them were females, but they had a king who was called "Gwydion ab Don". He lived among the stars in a place called Caer Gwydion. Generally he was thought of as kind and good, unlike his dark counterpart called Gwynn ap Nudd who inhabited the otherworld called *Annwn*. In some stories, however, Gwynn ap Nudd appears to be both King of the Fairies and King of Annwn.

King Gwydion had a queen called Gwenhidw, and maybe this name comes from the same root as Gwenhwyvar or Guinevere ("white appirition") who was the Queen of King Arthur. Early in the last century it was common for old people to refer to the fleece-like clouds which occur in fine weather as "the sheep of Gwenhidw." In other old fairy tales the fairy queen is called Mor Gwyn ("white maid'), and this is thought to be the origin of the name Morgan or Morgana.

There are a few Pembrokeshire stories about the King of the Fairies, but in them he is encountered only in Fairyland. The only story known to local people about the King of the Fairies straying into the world of the mortals is quite specifically about Gwynn ap Nudd.

One day St Collen was passing a period of mortification as a hermit under a rock up in the mountains. He overheard two men talking about Gwynn ap Nudd, in which one said to the other that Gwynn was the King of the Fairies. Collen cried out to the men and told them not to talk about devils. This made Gwynn very angry, for he greatly objected to being called a devil. He summoned the saint to meet him on a hill-top at noon, and after repeated refusals at last Collen turned up for the appointment, carrying with him a flask of holy water just in case of emergencies. When he arrived on the hill summit he saw a wonderful fairy castle, with well-ordered troops around it, and minstrels and singers making sweet music, and fine young men on steeds, and elegant and sprightly fairy maidens. He was enchanted by the peace and beauty of it all. He was invited to enter the castle, and on doing so he saw the King of the Fairies seated on a golden throne. The King welcomed Collen warmly and graciously, and invited him to sit down and share food with him.

"Come, my lord," said the King. "Let me offer you every

dainty and delicacy that the heart can desire, and every sweet liquor, and every courtesy and service, and every refined entertainment, and every choice gift, and every respect and welcome that should be due to a man of your great wisdom."

"I would not even eat the leaves of the trees in this place," replied Collen. "Come now, my lord," urged the King. "It is churlish to refuse my hospitality. Did you ever see such a palace? And did you ever see finer servants and kinsmen than mine, dressed as they are in red and blue?" "I know your wiles," said Collen. "And I know that the red signifies burning, and that the blue signifies coldness. Away with you and all your kind!"

And with that Collen took out his flask of holy water, and sprinkled it on the heads of the Fairy King and his kinsmen. In an instant the castle, the young men and maidens, the servants and the minstrels, and the Fairy King himself disappeared. And Collen stood alone on a green and peaceful hill-top amid the sounds of the birds and the whispering wind.

Date: c 1850   *Source: Wentz p 151; Sikes p 8*

4.6 Fairy Helpers for Dr Harries

There is a strange little tale about Dr Harries, the magician of Werndew (near Dinas), in which the great man is assisted in his divination by fairies. This is most unusual, since magicians were traditionally supposed to be in contact with the devil and his cohorts rather than with the *Tylwyth Teg*. However, the story is as follows. A farmer from near Carmarthen travelled to Werndew and explained to Dr Harries that he had lost his cattle. The magician immediately summoned the fairies, and explained that they were exceedingly clever at foretelling the future, discovering secrets, and finding lost property. So he consulted them about the lost cattle, and then told the farmer to go home as quickly as he could and look for them in a certain place. The magician described the place in so much detail that the farmer immediately recognized the spot, and referred to it by name. He rushed back to his farm near Carmarthen, went to the spot, and recovered his cattle.

Date: c 1850?   *Source: Wentz p 151*

PEMBROKESHIRE
FOLK TALES

WITCHCRAFT
AND
MAGIC

5.1 The Queen of the Pembrokeshire Witches

Dolly Llewellin was known as the Queen of the Pembrokeshire witches, and she was widely feared in the area around Carew Newton. She lived in a cottage on Rosemary Lane. One Saturday evening she was coming home from Pembroke market with a heavy basket full of provisions. Mr and Mrs Lloyd of Carew Newton were driving home along the same road in their heavily-laden trap, and they passed Dolly at Penny Bridge near Holyland. William Evans the blacksmith overheard the following conversation. "Come now," said Dolly to Mr Lloyd, "take me up, for I have a heavy basket." Mr Lloyd replied "I cannot, for I have a heavily laden trap as it is." "Ha!" she exclaimed in disgust, and asked him a second time. The reply was the same, as it was after a third request. At last she turned away and said "So be it then. The devil take you!"

     Mr and Mrs Lloyd continued up the hill towards Holyland House, but near the entrance gate of the mansion the linch pin fell out and the wheel dropped off the trap. The farmer and his wife were flung onto the road, and flour and groceries were scattered about over a wide area. William Evans helped them to clear up the mess and to get things back into the trap, and the wheel was secured in position. Mr Lloyd was furious. "You damned thundering old witch!" he shouted, taking up his horse whip. "If you don't take the curse off me this minute I'll murder you!" Dolly didn't look in the least abashed, and there followed a period of negotiation. At last he agreed to give her a lift if she said "God bless you!". This she did, somewhat reluctantly, and the curse having been lifted in this way the trap and its three occupants made the rest of the journey back to Carew Newton quite uneventfully.

Date: 1850   *Source: Newscuttings Vol 27, p 71*

5.2   The Hound of Hell at Hayscastle

Long ago there was a wild and violent young man who belonged to an ancient family in the eastern parts of Dewisland. He was immensely tall and sported a ferocious black beard. He had great strength and an uncontrollable temper, and he was greatly feared and disliked by all the local people. He was viewed very much as the black sheep of the family. He used to ride about the country lanes on a large horse, so heedless of other people's welfare that those who were in his way literally had to jump for their lives.

One evening while galloping madly along a lane on his way home from Haverfordwest, he knocked down and killed a little girl. Quickly her family and neighbours gathered round, and what with their cries and curses, and the oaths of the arrogant horseman, there was soon pandemonium. An old lady who lived in a nearby cottage heard all the commotion and came out to investigate. She had a reputation of being a witch (*gwrach or gwyddon*), and when she saw the dead child she told the bearded horseman that his soul was now in the hands of the evil one, and that when his time came to die Old Nick would send a huge black hound or *Gwyllgi* to curse him and his descendants. The young man laughed at this, tossed a few coins to the bereaved family to cover their loss, and set off on his way. Soon afterwards his family, mindful of the fact that he could be charged with murder, sent him abroad and nothing was heard of him for many years.

But about 40 years later a middle-aged man of great strength and forceful personality came into Solva on one of the vessels that plied the coastal trade. The most striking thing about him was his thick hair and long black beard. He left his ship and went to live in a small cottage, and he obtained work as a labourer with Mr Raymond, a prosperous Solva merchant. He was still good-looking, and was clearly well educated; and in time he took a young wife who bore him several children. He gained a reputation for the shortness of his temper, and became involved in a number of fist fights. Gradually people started to recognize the physical and emotional traits of the ancient family in him, and some began to suspect that he was the "missing younger son" who had gone abroad from the Hayscastle area many years before. Finally he admitted to his origins during a night of revelry in a local tavern, and then stormed out, swearing that he would be more content to ride down all those present than drink with them. Then he slammed the door, and was gone into the night.

A fortnight later the man's young wife ran to the door of the local doctor in a state of shock. She pleaded with him to come to the cottage quickly; so he threw on his coat and followed her. When he came into the bedroom the man was on the bed with his limbs thrashing about horribly and with an awful expression of terror on his face. He kept shouting hysterically "Keep the dog away! Keep the dog away!" Nobody could control him or subdue him. This went on for some time, until at last his voice trailed away to a whisper, and he fell back dead. He was buried at Tregroes graveyard.

Succeeding generations of the old man's family were all haunted by the spectral hound; and the last head of the family to die, in 1923, was actually pursued by it one night in a lane near Hayscastle.

Date: c 1750   *Source: Francis Jones, Newscuttings, Vol 27, p 64*

5.3 In Trouble with the Law

The most famous of all the West Wales magicians were Dr John Harries of Cwrt-y-Cadno in Carmarthenshire and his son Henry who also carried on this strange trade. There are innumerable stories about the special powers of "Old Dr Harries", in particular, in lifting curses, foretelling the future, solving mysteries and finding lost animals. He was reputed to be in touch with the spirit world, where his contacts brough him into grave danger on many occasions. He died in 1839.

    The case which brought Dr Harries his first recognition in the community involved a quite difficult confrontation with the law. Around the year 1800 a young woman of Llandeilo disappeared. She was engaged to be marrieed, and her sweetheart and family searched high and low for her without success. Many of the neighbours also helped, and requests for information were sent out over a wide area. No evidence of her whereabouts could be found. At last her parents went to see Dr Harries at Cwrt-y-Cadno. At that time he did not have any great reputation, but he had helped some people with their problems, and the poor demented parents had to try every possible avenue that might lead them to a solution of their terrible mystery.

    On hearing the details, Dr Harries consulted his magic books and then informed them as follows. The poor girl, he said, was dead. She had been murdered by her sweetheart, and was buried in the mid-day shade of a certain tree. He did not know the name of the place, but he could describe it exactly. The tree stood alone near a brook, and in the hollow of the tree there was a bee's nest.

    The poor parents were naturally horrified to hear this news, but when Dr Harries had consoled them as best he could, they returned home and instituted a further search. Neighbours scoured the countryside around Llandeilo until they found the spot described by the magician, and there they found a shallow grave containing the body of the murdered girl. The murderer had fled, but he was eventually found and arrested. He confessed to the crime, and was in due course executed.

    When the court case was complete, the legal authorities took it into their heads to charge Dr Harries with being an accomplice to the crime, for they could not conceive of any way in which he could have known the girl's burial place other then through direct involvement. Local people were outraged, for they were perfectly prepared to believe that the doctor had the power of *rhamanta* or magic divination. But in the face of much local hostility the magistrates, Mr

Lloyd of Glansevin and Mr Glyn of Glanbran, persisted. They summoned the doctor at the magistrates court in Llandovery, where he was duly charged. But there was not a scrap of evidence against him. When the proceedings dragged on, Dr Harries at last started to get angry with the stupid questions which the magistrates were asking. He said "Your Honours, I fear that we are getting nowhere in this matter. If you wish me to demonstrate my powers for you, I suggest we do the following. If you will both tell me the date and the hour on which you were born, I will tell you immediately the date and the hour upon which you will die."

At this, the magistrates both came out in a cold sweat. They suddenly decided that the matter had gone far enough, and dismissed the case. Dr Harries returned to Cwrt-y-Cadno a local hero, with his reputation well and truly made.

Date: c 1800   *Source: Davies p 253*

5.4 The Case of the Missing Cows

One story of wizardry which was very well known in Pembrokeshire tells of a farmer from the Pendine area who lost three cows. Having searched in vain for them., he went at last to see Dr John Harries at Cwrt-y-Cadno. The great *Consuriwr* or magician listened intently to his story, but then said that he could not solve the problem immediately. He would need a little time, he said, to consult his magic books and his contacts in the spirit world. He suggested that the farmer should find lodgings in the neighbourhood for the night, and then come back next morning. This the farmer agreed to do.

Having taken his leave of the great man, the farmer was wondering where he might find some accommodation. But then, in crossing the yard outside Dr Harries' house, he noticed a barn nearby which looked as if it might provide him with a nice dry bed for the night. He looked inside, and found that it was half full of sweet dry hay. So he settled down quietly in the hay and went to sleep.

About one o'clock in the morning the farmer was awakened by the footsteps of Dr Harries coming into the barn. He carried a lantern in his hand, which he put down on the floor in the middle of a clearing in the hay. The farmer hardly dared to breathe, and snuggled down deeply into the hay for fear of being discovered. But then, as he watched, Dr Harries drew a circle around himself in the dust of the barn floor, opened a big magic book, and made an incantation which had the effect of summoning seven spirits. They came one by one, in the shapes of assorted animals and humans and strange demons; and as each one appeared he asked "Where are the farmer's missing cows?" Some of the spirits appeared quite stupid, and the doctor became irritated with them when they gave no help at all. One of the spirits, when asked the question, replied "A pig in the hay". This made the farmer greatly alarmed, since he was convinced that Dr Harries would take the hint and discover him in his hiding-place. But he did not, and the tense moment passed.

At last the seventh spirit, on being pressed by the doctor, shouted out "The farmer's cows will be on Carmarthen Bridge at 12 o'clock tomorrow." Satisfied at last, the doctor smiled and dismissed all the spirits. Then he stepped outside the circle, picked up his lantern, and went off to bed.

The farmer was so excited that he could not sleep. He now knew the answer to his problem, and thought that he might as well save on the magician's fee; so as soon as he saw the first light of dawn driving the darkness from the eastern sky he crept out and hurried back to Carmarthen. It was a long walk, but he got there just before noon. As predicted, his three cows were crossing the bridge, driven by a stranger who was intent upon selling them at Carmarthen market. He challenged the man, who ran off. Delighted, he turned the cows round and started to drive them homewards.

However, he had progressed no more than half a mile when all three cows collapsed at the side of the road, more dead than alive. The farmer, whose conscience had been troubling him about evading the magician's fee, became convinced that the cows were bewitched. So he had to leave the animals where they were and make the long trek all the way back to Cwrt-y-Cadno. The doctor was waiting for him. "Serve thee right," he said, wagging his finger. "I have bewitched thy cattle as a punishment for running away without paying me for my information from the spirit world. Now, if you pay me, all will be well with thy three cows." The farmer had no option but to pay the fee, and on returning to the cows he found them on their feet, happily eating buttercups at the side of the road.

Date: c 1830   *Source: Davies p 255*

5.5 Rescue on Frenni Fawr

Almost 150 years ago a young shepherd boy was looking after the sheep on Freni Fawr, not far from Crymych. Unfortunately he stepped into a fairy ring, and disappeared. When he did not return home his parents went looking for him, and when they discovered the circle of mushrooms they feared the worst. Not knowing what to do, they decided to consult the famous *dyn hysbys* (magician) Dr Joseph Harries, who lived in a cottage at Werndew, near Dinas. So the father set off to visit him.

Dr Harries heard his story in silence, and then he shook his head. "I do not think I can help," he said gravely. "It is said that those who are taken to fairyland might as well be left there, for if they are rescued they are sure to die, having become used to fairy foods and fairy living."

But the father of the missing boy was adamant. "At the moment we have no son anyway," he said. "If we rescue him and he then dies, we are no worse off. And at least we will have the small compensation of knowing that we did what we could."

So Dr Harries reluctantly agreed to help, and told the father that he and his wife must return to exactly the spot where their son had disappeared, exactly a year after his disappearance and exactly at the time when the sun was at its highest point in the heavens. They would see their son dancing inside an enchanted circle with the *Tylwyth Teg*. They must stand outside the circle, taking care not to touch it. They must wait until the boy came dancing close to them, and then they were to grab hold of his coat tails and pull him out. "After that, I cannot control what happens," said the magician, "for the powers of the fairy folk are great indeed."

So the boy's parents did exactly as they were instructed. And it came to pass just as the magician had predicted. Once outside the ring, the boy looked surprised and then disappointed, and said: "Oh father, you have spoiled my pleasure." His mother ran up to embrace him and console him, but as she reached him he disintegrated into a small heap of ashes at her feet.

Date: c 1830   *Source: Francis Green Newscuttings, Vol 11 p 151*

5.6 Gwen Davies the White Witch

In 1937 a woman called Gwen Davies was at work in and around a South Pembrokeshire village, helping to heal the sick. Locally she was referred to as a white witch, but today we would refer to her as a charmer. One old man, who had been receiving medical attention for years but with no satisfactory result, was prevailed upon by his family to go and visit Gwen. This he did, and when he had explained the nature of his ailment and the treatment he had received, she sat him down in a chair with a table in front of it. She placed 11 little pieces of straw on the table. Then she took a longer straw and waved it around the patient's head several times. Then she went to the table and moved one of the little pieces of straw. She repeated the "treatment" with the long straw, and then moved another of the short pieces to another part of the table. This went on for a long time, until all of the little pieces of straw had been moved from their original positions. Each time she went to the table, Gwen mumbled some words (they appeared to be Biblical quotations) in a low voice. Then, the treatment over, she announced: "You will get well now, but it will take time. Eat all you can get, but mind you don't touch no doctor's medicines, and definitely no hard drink." Gwen would take no payment for her ministrations. The patient left, did as he was told, and eventually was completely cured.

Date: 1937   *Source: W. Tel. Almanac 1937*

5.7 Nasty Fright at Pen Palis

Mr Peter Denzil Edwards recently recalled a story which was told to
him as a child. It concerned his grandparents, who lived at Dan Coed
in the Gwaun Valley in the early part of this century.

The tale concerns a bend in the road at the end of the
mountain ridge of Pen Palis, and not far from Morvil. The bend,
between the farms of Trepant and March-pres, has been known for
many years as "The Devil's Bend," and in the old days travellers
would always pass that way with a certain sense of foreboding.
Indeed, the whole area around Morvil was renowned for its
connections with the supernatural, and for sightings of battles in the
sky (see Volume I, stories 7.10 and 7.11).

It was a wet and windy night, and Mr and Mrs Edwards were
on their way home to Dan Coed from the New Inn. They were
travelling, as usual, by pony and trap. As they approached the bend
in the darkness they were just able to make out the roadway ahead of
them, and suddenly they became aware of something rather shapeless
coming over the hedge. Before they could stop the pony the "thing"

had moved along silently and had passed under the trap. It then moved along the road behind them until they could see it no more in the darkness. The pony was very frightened, and so were Mr and Mrs Edwards. "Oh Lydia," said the old man. "That was the devil. We've seen him tonight."

But Lydia was made of sterner stuff, and she said "Stop the pony here. I'm going back to see what that was." And she scuttled off back along the road. A few minutes later she turned up with a dark green and nicely rounded gorse bush stuck on the tip of her walking stick. "There's your devil!" she said; and the couple continued on their journey, greatly relieved.

Afterwards they ascertained that the local farmer had been cutting gorse or furze for animal fodder in the field adjacent to the road, and had left some cut bushes behind. In the strong wind one of these bushes had rolled over the hedge and had bounced off down the road, just like the tumbleweed of the Wild West of America.

Date: c 1910   *Source : Peter Denzil Edwards*

5.8 The Flying Witch of Marloes

There is not a single reference in the folk tale literature of Pembrokeshire to a witch actually flying through the air on a broomstick. For the most part their special powers are restricted to transformations into animals such as cats and hares, and placing curses on machines or individuals. However, a recent story from Marloes has proved the exception to the rule.

A local gentleman called David was making a telephone call from the village phone box one evening at about 9 pm. It was a dark evening, and the street lights were lit. Having finished his call, he was leaving the phone box when he saw, quite clearly, a witch on a broomstick flying across the road in front of him. She was about 10 ft above the road surface, and as David watched she swooped up towards the roof of a house next to the Two Foxes public house and simply appeared to pass into the roof. And so she disappeared from sight. David was so surprised that he did not make a note of her clothing; but he recalls that it was dark in colour.

The observer was not particularly frightened by the encounter, but recalls that he was rather disappointed that the witch had not gone into his roof instead, where maybe he could later on have had an interesting chat with her.

Date: 1992   *Source: word of mouth*

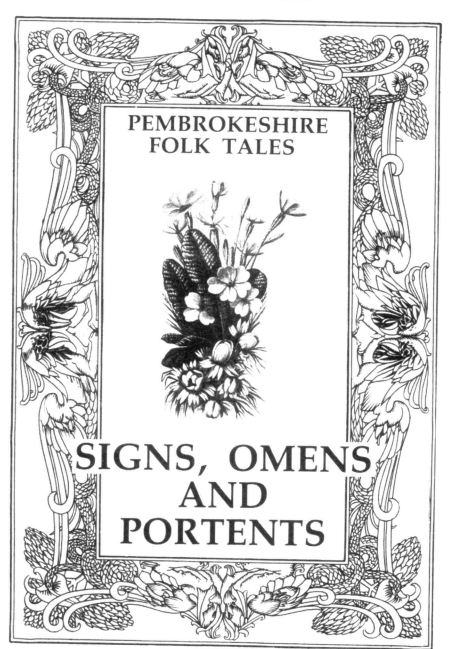

PEMBROKESHIRE
FOLK TALES

SIGNS, OMENS AND PORTENTS

6.1   Spirit Funeral at Cresswell Quay

In the middle of the last century one John Davies, who lived in Oakhill
Lane, Cresswell Quay, was on his way down to the quay. It was a
velvet-black night with a garland of stars across the heavens.
Suddenly Mr Davies got caught up in the middle of a phantom
funeral procession. He was so crushed and knocked about that he
said afterwards that he had been frightened for his life. There was a
white light in the front of the funeral. At last the phantom crowd of
mourners went past and John was able to continue on his way in
peace and quiet. Some days later a local person died, and a funeral
accompanied by a great throng of people passed along this same
road, exactly as John Davies had experienced it. The only thing
missing was the bright light at the head of the procession.

Date: c.1860   *Source: H.C. Tierney, Newscuttings, Vol 27, p 71*

6.2 The Corpse Candles at Pendine

There are a number of records of the *Canwyll Gorff* or corpse candle in
the Laugharne - Pendine area. Around 1850 an old gentleman of
Laugharne, belonging to a most respectable family, was walking one
evening towards St Clears in the company of a friend.   Both men
were surprised to see two lights moving across a field towards the
Pilgrim Church down by the river. As they watched, the lights went
into the church. On another occasion the old man saw a phantom
funeral or *Toili* go into the same church.

Some years later a woman belonging to one of the best-known
families in the village of Pendine was visited by her brother and his
young son. Suddenly, at about eleven o'clock in the morning, the little
boy was seized by a very severe fever. The doctor was called and did
what he could, but by evening the child had shown little sign of
recovery. The boy's father was distraught, and he was at last
encouraged by his sister to go outside for a breath of fresh air while
she continued to nurse the patient.   While he was walking back and
forth in front of the house, the father's attention was attracted by a

small light in the churchyard. It crossed the churchyard and went into the church. Later it came out again and travelled through the churchyard to the position of the family tomb. There it stopped. Very shortly afterwards the child died. When the funeral took place the little boy was buried in exactly the spot where the *Toili* had stopped.

The boy's father had previously refused to believe in corpse candles and other omens and portents; but after this tragic experience he was forced to admit that such things really existed.

Another member of the same family, also living in Pendine, was married to a man who fell seriously ill. He was growing weaker each day, and his wife spent much time sitting with him in the bedroom. One day she looked out through the bedroom window and said "Oh, look! There is a curious little light down there on the Strand. What on earth can it be?" The husband raised himself on his pillow and said "I know what it is, my dear. It is the light before death. It is for me." And very shortly afterwards he passed away.

Date: c 1860   *Source: Curtis p 216*

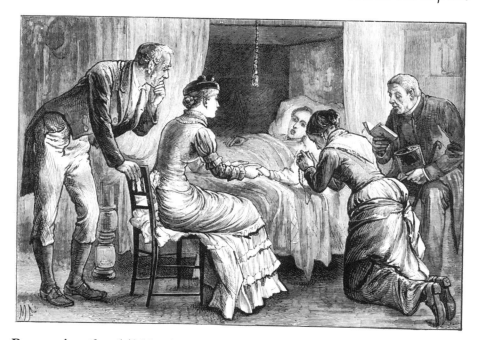

By evening the child had shown little sign of recovery ......

6.3 Fetch Funeral at St David's

Mr Pavin Phillips of Haverfordwest had a good friend who was a clergyman in St David's. One of his parishioners was an old woman called Molly who frequently observed phantom funerals. After church she would say to him "Ay ay, Reverend fach, you'll be here of a weekday soon, for I saw a funeral last night." And her predictions were always fulfilled. However, the clergyman remained sceptical, and on one occasion he asked her "Well, Molly, have you seen a funeral lately?" "Ay,ay, Reverend fach," came the reply. "I saw one a night or two ago. but there's a strange thing. You did something I never seen before."

"Why, what was that?" inquired the minister.

"Well, as you met up with the procession you stooped down and picked something up off the ground."

"Fancy that," thought the clergyman to himself. "I'll try you out this time, Molly, and see if I can't make a liar of you for once."

Some time afterwards the clergyman was summoned to a funeral at a nearby village. He arrived on horseback, and as he dismounted to meet the mourners he caught his surplice in his spur and in the ensuing tangle dropped some possessions onto the ground. As he bent down to pick them up a picture of old Molly entered his mind, with a sly smile on her face....

Date: c 1880?
Source: Newscuttings, Vol 27, p 64

One of his parishioners was an old woman called Molly who frequently observed phantom funerals........

6.4 Mr Severn meets the Ceffyl Pren

One of the oldest folk customs in Pembrokeshire was to subject adulterers or philanderers (or even nagging wives) to local ridicule through the use of *y ceffyl pren* or "the wooden horse". This was an effigy made of straw or other material (sometimes labelled with the offending person's name) which was mounted on a pole or seated in a chair and then paraded around the community on a ladder. The whole contraption would be carried around on men's shoulders, and there would be a noisy procession involving all the neighbours singing, dancing, shouting, and beating on saucepans for all they were worth.

Halting at intervals, the members of the procession, and any others who were within earshot, would be treated to a little poem by the leader. For example, he might say:

Ran-dan-dan!
Betty Morris have beat her man.
And what was it with?
With a rake or a reel?
No, never it was,
But with an old poker
That made him squeal!

If you offended against the strong sense of morality and natural justice that existed in small communities, you could expect to be pilloried in this way. A rowdy mob outside your front door, followed by a ceremonial burning of your effigy in the street, was sometimes enough to get you to mend your ways. In other cases, for example in the event of infidelity, the offending man and woman would be taken from their homes, roped up back to back, and paraded around the community on the *ceffyl pren*, to be jeered at by the neighbours and pelted with rotten eggs and tomatoes. Then the frightened and bedraggled offenders would be released at their respective dwellings and driven indoors with further shouts and screams of derision.

Possibly the last occasion on which the *ceffyl pren* was used in Pembrokeshire was around 1850 in Amroth. An unfaithful husband, one Mr Severn of Craig-y-borrian, was having a fairly public affair with a lady working as a governess in the big house. One day he was captured by a mob, trussed up, placed on a stool and carried around the village on the ladder. This was at the instigation of his enraged wife. He was subjected to great abuse, pelted with missiles and delivered back to his wife very much the worse for wear. However, far from mending his ways, Mr Severn eloped the following day with the governess, and was never seen in the village again.

Date: 1850   *Source: Howells p 101*

6.5 Jumping to Conclusions

In the old days there were so many tales of corpse candles, phantom funerals and other strange signs and omens that almost everybody in the country districts expected to encounter such things at some stage in their lives.

One winter's evening around the year 1830, two ladies belonging to the family of Mr Richard Mason were returning home to Tenby from a visit to Narberth market. They were much delayed on their journey, and it was well after midnight when they reached home in their hired carriage. The other members of the family, who had been rather anxious because of their late arrival, rushed to the door to receive them, and others went to the windows with their candles when they heard the sound of the horses' hooves and carriage wheels on the gravel of the driveway. By the light of several lanterns, the ladies were helped down from the carriage, and after unloading their shopping the coachman set off towards his coach-house and stables, passing the churchyard on the way before disappearing behind the high hedge.

The next morning Mr Mason's gardener George was approached by an old man from the nearby village, who gravely informed him that a death was imminent in the family. "Now where didst tha get that idea from?" asked the gardener. "Not a shadow of doubt about it, me friend," replied the old man, sidling up to him and whispering into his ear. "I seen the lights!"

The gardener inquired as to what lights these might have been. The old man glanced over his shoulder, as if afraid that he was being watched by the evil eye. Then he continued, speaking in a low hoarse voice. "The lights was here last night, sure as eggs is eggs," he said. "In the early mornin' hour it was, when all good folks is fast asleep."

"The corpse candles was at the doors and windows of the big house, and -- Heaven help the poor soul soon to be called to the Lord's bosom -- I even seen the phantom hearse lit up with ghostly lights. It come down the drive to the front door. There was big phantom horses pullin' it. An' I seen for meself that they galloped off up the drive to the churchyard, an' then disappeared! Then I looked back at the big house, an' the corpse candles had all gone. Nothin' left but the black black night an' the winter wind moanin' in the trees. Oh, terrible, terrible it was! When I watched me knees was quakin' an' I come out in a cold sweat. Even now, when I thinks of it, the hairs is standin' up on the back o' me neck." And with a final furtive glance over his shoulder, the old man concluded "You mark my words, George, death will strike this household afore the week is done. The lights is never wrong!"

The prophet of doom was greatly disappointed when George told him about the circumstances surrounding the very late return of the two ladies from their shopping expedition to Narberth.

Date: c 1830   *Source: Bielski, 1979; Mason, 1858*

6.6 Fetch Funeral for a Minister

Around the year 1880 a nonconformist minister invited a colleague (who was also a reverend gentleman) from a neighbouring village to pay him a visit. Probably he was due to act as guest preacher in the village chapel on the following day, and the local minister booked a bedroom for his guest above a little shop. He arrived safely enough, but being an elderly man who was not in the best of health he decided to retire to bed early.

Downstairs the shopkeeper was making up his books after the week's trading when he was terrified to see two carpenters (whom he recognized) coming downstairs from the bedroom carrying a coffin. Without saying a word they opened the front door, carried their burden out of the shop, and disappeared.

The poor shopkeeper was so frightened that he hardly slept a wink that night, and in the morning, when his guest came downstairs, he related what he had seen. They were discussing the possibility that this might have been a "fetch funeral" when the local minister came to see his friend. So the shopkeeper narrated the strange tale all over again, at which the new arrival uttered a strange cry, threw up his hands and staggered backwards.

Before the guest and the shopkeeper could do anything the minister collapsed "in a fit of apoplexy". The two men immediately carried him upstairs and laid him down on the bed which had been occupied in the night by his friend. And there he died, before they could send a message for the local doctor.

Although it was now a Sunday, the doctor came along and confirmed that the minister was dead, and the village undertaker was asked to make arrangements. Later in the day two carpenters arrived, bearing a coffin. They were the same two carpenters seen by the shopkeeper in his vision. They put the body inside, carried the burden downstairs, opened the door of the shop, and went outside en route to the minister's own house. Everything that happened was exactly as foreseen by the shopkeeper the previous evening.

Date: c 1880   *Source: Laws, 1888, p 413*

6.7 Phantom Funeral at New Hedges

According to tradition, a phantom funeral used to haunt the junction near Twy Cross, where the road to Saundersfoot branched off the Tenby - Narberth road. On still and moonless nights, precisely at midnight, a ghostly cortege was often heard and sometimes seen. The first thing to be heard would be the sound of horses' hooves. Then a hearse would appear in a faint whitish glow, followed by several closed carriages and a crowd of people on foot. The people would be dressed in long black coats, with the men wearing tall Victorian hats. The procession would take some time to go past, and then it would all fade away, according to the locals, "like mist before the sun." On other occasions dogs and other animals would sense the presence of something unseen by human beings.

This same phantom funeral was still being seen around 1936, but there are no recorded recent sightings, and we may speculate that all the modern roadworks on the A478, and all the horrible noisy traffic, have frightened the phantoms away.

Date: 1936   *Source: Francis Green Newscuttings, Vol 16 p 69*

6.8   The Haunting of John Mathias

A Pembrokeshire man called John Mathias once caused himself great trouble following the death of his wife Martha. He knew that she had not completed a proper will, so while her corpse was still warm he placed a pen in her hand and then directed it with his own hand so that it wrote out a brief will leaving all her worldly possessions to him. At the foot of the page he wrote "signed by my own hand, Martha Mathias." Afterwards he swore on oath that he had seen his wife write out the will, and so he inherited all her savings and her property.

Later John Mathias married again, and immediately he was afflicted with signs and hauntings. Strange noises occurred in the house, crockery was flung about and broken, doors were locked and unlocked by unseen hands, candles were extinguished and Mr Mathias and his new wife became very scared. They sold the house and moved to another - but still the hauntings continued. Even in chapel, where he was a deacon, the poor man would sometimes rise to his feet in the middle of a sermon and would appear to be struggling with some unseen adversary. Naturally, this caused great consternation among his fellow worshippers. So troubled was he that the air seemed to chill when he approached, and his children became very disturbed.

At last the foolish man recognized the reason for the haunting; he gave away all his wife's money and possessions to other relatives, and from that day on he was troubled no more.

Date: c. 1850?   *Source: W. Tel. Almanac 1955*

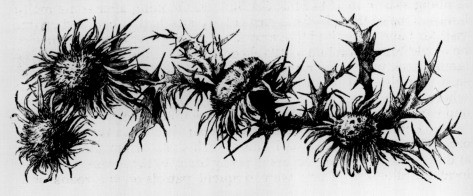

6.9 Corpse Candles at Walton West

In 1899 an old man from Walton West related that, when he was a boy, he and his younger brother were in bed one night, pinching one another and generally fooling about (as boys will) before going to sleep. Suddenly he saw a peculiar light on the bed. He stopped his horseplay and drew his brother's attention to it; but the other child could see nothing. He then hit the light with his hand, upon which it "went into a thousand fragments" before reforming into its original shape. Then the light gradually disappeared. Some days later a visitor to the house was given the boy's bedroom to sleep in, and died during the night just where the corpse candle had been seen.

Date: 1830   *Source: Francis Green News Cuttings 12, p 92*

6.10 The Haunted Bell

This tragic tale was told to Francis Jones in the 1920s by a very old resident of Llandeloy, near Solva. In the old man's cottage Mr Jones noticed a battered sheep-bell hanging on the wall, and was told that it used to be haunted.

According to the old man, young Mr James of Lochmeyler met Miss Griffiths of Treindeg at Tancredston Fair. They were immediately attracted to one another, and began courting. Often Mr James would ride over to Treindeg to see his beloved. During the lambing season in 1644 Miss Griffiths was looking after some molly lambs. One of them became particularly attached to her, and on one visit Mr James promised that next time he rode over from Lochmeyler he would bring with him a little sheep bell that could be tied round the lamb's neck with a red ribbon. The young lady was enchanted, and said that the bell would be more than a means of knowing the whereabouts of her pet lamb - it would be a symbol of their love, and would remind her of her beloved every time it rang.

Before young Mr James' next visit there was turmoil in the area. Cromwell's troops had taken Roch Castle from the Royalists and in order to quell any future uprising many of them were billeted in local farmhouses. There were frequent patrols on the roads and

Often Mr James would ride over to Treindeg to see his beloved...

trackways. It was dangerous to travel at night, and the Roundheads said they would shoot anybody who was about after dark. However, love knows no restraint and young Mr James became desperate to see his beloved Miss Griffiths again. So, one evening, he set off for Treindeg - on foot, since this would attract less attention. After a long and muddy journey cross-country he could see the lights of Treindeg ahead of him - but as he approached in the darkness he fell into a ditch and got very wet. The little bell which he held in his hand rang gently, disturbing the silence of the night. Unconcerned, he pressed on, but he was challenged by some dark shadows on the nearby road. Foolishly, he did not stop and answer, but ran on towards the lights of the house where Miss Griffiths would be waiting for him. As he did so the bell in his hand rang again. A volley of shots rang out, and the young man fell and died face-down in the mud.

The commotion attracted the people of Treindeg, and they all came out with lanterns. They found a group of Parliamentary soldiers standing over the body of the dead man. Miss Griffiths came too, and in the dim light of the lanterns she was composed enough to kiss the forehead of her dead lover and to take the sheep-bell from his hand. Mr James was buried a few days later, and within a few months Miss Griffiths was dead also, the victim of a broken heart.

Some years later the old house of Treindeg was burned down in a terrible fire, and among the ashes afterwards a workman picked up the burnt and battered sheep bell. He took it away and it remained in his family for many generations. All the family knew that the spirit of young Mr James resided in the bell, for occasionally it would ring of its own accord. The old man who related this tale to Francis Jones heard it only once, when it rang gently at midnight (on the anniversary of the young man's death) for a minute or so. After that the old man took out the tongue of the bell, and he felt that it - and the restless spirit of the young lover - had been at rest ever since.

Date: 1644   *Source: Francis Jones Newscuttings, Vol 27, p 91*

6.11 No Place for Horses

Mr JW Phillips recorded in 1920 that when he was a small boy he went out in the family carriage with his father and two sisters, from Haverfordwest to Broad Haven. On a straight stretch of road across Lamborough Moor, before Fowl Bridge, on a bright sunny day with nothing untoward to be seen, the horse suddenly stopped and refused to go on. He seemed to be staring at something on the road in front of him, and was clearly trembling and terrified. Mr Phillips senior said to the coach driver "What on earth is the matter with him? Why doesn't he go on?" The driver said "I don't know, sir. Horses often do the same sort of thing, precisely at this spot." After a great deal of cajoling, the horse at last crossed the spot and continued.

Some years later, as a young man, JW Phillips was riding the same way when his pony suddenly shied and turned back, throwing him out of the saddle. He had great difficulty in recapturing the horse and getting it to continue. The same thing happened to one of his sisters on another occasion, and also to his mother. On one occasion the horse could not be induced to pass the spot even though it was heading for home. Mrs Phillips had to take the horse home by quite a different route.

Date: c. 1920   *Source: J.W. Phillips ms No 133*

6.12 Presentiment at Tenby

JW Phillips was staying in Tenby for a weekend with an elderly gentleman who was a family friend. Several others had been invited for a house party, and together the guests, under the benign eye of their host, spent a pleasant two days of conversation and entertainment. On the morning of his departure, JW Phillips was sitting in the old man's garden when he sensed somebody coming up behind him and saying "The next time you come here will be the old man's funeral." He turned quickly, and there was no-one there.

Soon afterwards Mr Phillips said farewell and left for home in Haverfordwest. He was haunted by the strange premonition, and could not get it out of his mind. Later the same afternoon the old man went out for a drive in his carriage. Suddenly the horse bolted; he was thrown out of the carriage and was seriously injured. He died from his injuries the following Thursday. In the event Mr Phillips could not attend the funeral because of another previous engagement, but for the rest of his life the incident in the garden remained fixed in his memory.

Date: 1913   *Source: JW Phillips ms No 133*

6.13   All Hallow's Eve in a Country House

JW Phillips's mother once related to him a strange story of an old friend of hers. It happened around the year 1850. She and her friend were staying in a large old house in the Pembrokeshire countryside together with various other young ladies. It was All Hallow's Eve, and the talk turned excitedly to ghosts, and witches, and strange phenomena. The bravest of the young ladies suddenly decided that she would try out a well-known superstition. The others tried to discourage her, but she persisted. She retired to her room and placed an article of her clothing on a chair in front of the fire. Then she settled down to watch.

Around midnight, when the house was very quiet, the girl became aware of a large man clad in oilskins, dripping wet, coming into the house. He looked at her intently. She was very frightened, for he had a fierce and forbidding expression. Then he turned on his heels and hurried out, slamming the door behind him. The hostess, and the other young girls, had been at the top of the stairs, but they neither saw nor heard anything except for a loud crash when the phantom visitor went out through the front door into the night. The girl fled from the downstairs room in a terrified state, and begged the others never to try that particular experiment for themselves. She took a long time to recover from the experience.

Some months later the same young lady was in the capital city, going over London Bridge. She looked across the street and saw the same man, dressed in the same wet oilskins. It was as if he had come up from one of the ships at the riverside. This time he was clearly no phantom, but made of flesh and blood. He was staring at her. She dared not return his gaze, feeling very alarmed and confused. Without looking back, she rushed on to her destination, her thoughts in a whirl. But later she met the same man at a dance. He had a

The poor girl was fated to be unhappy, for her husband turned out to be a cruel and ill-tempered man.

surly expression on his face, and she thought him very ugly.   She tried to avoid him, but he came up to her and asked her to dance, and although she wanted to refuse he held a sort of fatal attraction for her and she heard herself saying yes. They danced several times on that first evening, and went out frequently after that. Eventually they got married, although the girl's friends were all convinced that it was anything but a love match.

The poor girl was fated to be unhappy, for her new husband turned out to be a cruel and ill-tempered man. Her married life was one of constant pain and distress - a fact which she always blamed on the fateful experiment many years before on All Hallow's Eve.

Date: c 1850   *Source: JW Phillips ms No 133*

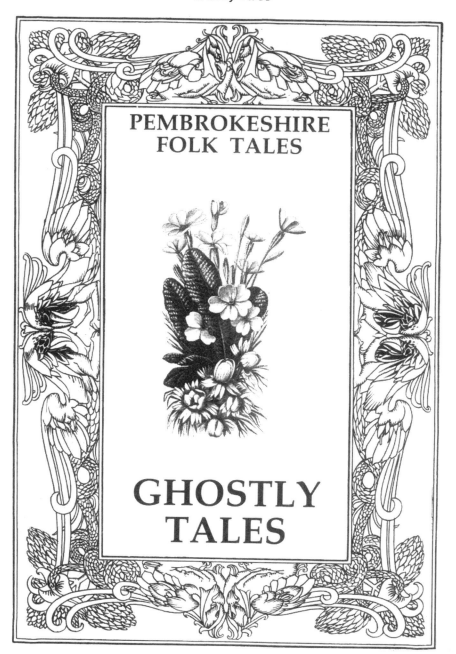

PEMBROKESHIRE
FOLK TALES

GHOSTLY
TALES

7.1 Ghostly Rebuke in Newport

Old Mrs Griffiths used to have a bakery and general store at Gwalia, in East Street, Newport. Sadly, her husband committed suicide, and she never got over the shock. She gave up the shop and moved to a house in Upper St Mary Street in the town, and there she lived for many years until she died. She was a very severe and devout woman -- a pillar of the local chapel community, a stickler for convention, and a strict upholder of propriety. She would be seen every Sunday on her way to Chapel, dressed in black, with her bible under her arm.

When she died her house came into the ownership of a relative who decided to let it out to tenants. And so a young couple moved in. The man was from the locality, but the young lady was from Essex. They dressed rather strangely and had peculiar hair-styles, and in those far-off and unenlightened days they were referred to by the locals as "hippies." Gradually it emerged that they were not actually married, and that this was a situation that did not worry them in the slightest.

But one day the young lady came to see a well-known councillor who also ran a long-established ironmongery in the town. "We're very worried," she said. "We love the house, but we think it is haunted. Every now and then we see this old lady in the house. She stands on the landing outside our bedroom door. She is of medium height, has a rather severe expression on her face, and she is dressed all in black. She seems to be holding a book under her arm. Normally she just stands there for a bit and then she disappears. It's almost as if she's standing there giving us a ghostly rebuke."

The councillor felt the hairs stand up on the back of his neck, as he immediately recognized the description as that of the recently-deceased Mrs Griffiths. All he could assume was that the old lady, who was not a happy person at the best of times, was offended and angry in her spirit world at the sight of two happy young people living and loving together out of wedlock. The councillor agreed to help, and eventually the Rector of the parish came and conducted an exorcism which removed the ghostly old lady from the house. Now the house feels as friendly and warm as any other in Newport.

Date: 1975   *Source: word of mouth*

7.2 The Lavender Lady of Newport Castle

Most castles have a reputation for hauntings, but Newport castle has a ghost who appears more benign than most. There are people in the town who claim to have seen "the white lady" on the lawns in front of the castle, but more frequently she is referred to locally as "the Lavender Lady". When Mr and Mrs Dean Shields were tenants of the castle they would often smell lavender very strongly, even though there was no lavender in bloom and no lavender scent in the building. On one occasion Mr Robert Humfrey was sleeping in the castle when he woke up to find an old lady standing at the foot of his bed. He was not at all frightened, and felt that she was actually a kind and gentle person.

She may also appear in a very old cottage near the castle. Quite recently a young man named John, who shared this cottage with his girl-friend, was visited by his brother and his family. The visitors knocked on the door, and when it was opened by John the visitors saw three people and not two in the passageway. John turned and he also saw "an apparition" standing behind his girl-friend. The three people who saw it described it as "a misty or shady presence." John had previously assumed that there was some spiritual inhabitant of the cottage, since occasionally lights would be turned on and off in approved ghostly fashion.

Date: 1992 *Source: word of mouth*

Newport Castle has a ghost who appears more benign then most...

7.3 The Ghost in the Crypt

At the top of High Street in Haverfordwest there is an old crypt which is thought to have been associated with a monastic house of some sort. There used to be a number of buildings on the corner of Market Street and High Street; one of them was occupied by a chandler in the last century, who used to store his candles in the crypt. Around 1860 there was a watch-maker's shop here, occupied

by a Mr Watson. The shop window was closed each evening by a boy employed by Mr Watson; he had to put up the heavy shutters over the glass and lock up before going home. The twilight was almost gone, and dark shadows were creeping across the street. The boy put up one shutter and went into the dark shop to fetch the second, when he suddenly saw the figure of a robed monk in front of him. So frightened was he that he dropped the shutter with a crash and fled home, leaving the shutters and the shop to look after themselves.

About ten years later, when some building operations were going on at the back of Commerce House in High Street, a well was found, with a very old skeleton at the bottom of it. In the 1920's a schoolboy from the nearby grammar school saw a monk in a dark habit standing on a wall near the crypt, surrounded by a blue light. There was another sighting of a monk by a workman. When Frederick Warren investigated these ghostly episodes in the 1920's he was told by a local confectioner of a local tradition that a monk had once been executed in the yard at the rear of his shop.

Date: 1860   *Source: Newscuttings, Vol 27, p 21*

7.4 The Black Monk of Caldey Island

In the 1920's there was great interest in the supernatural on Caldey Island, and there were various reports about this time of a mysterious "Glastonbury treasure", of strange sounds at dead of night, and of sightings of a black-habited monk in the lane near the old priory. Many local people are reputed to have seen him; they believed, in the old days, that he was the ghost of a monk who went mad. Aelred Carlyle, who had bought the island in 1906 for the use of his Anglican Benedictine community of monks, claimed to have seen the shadowy figure on many occasions. Other inhabitants of the island also reported seeing the apparition, which would appear out of nowhere and disappear quite suddenly.

One story linked the phantom monk with the Glastonbury Treasure, which is said to have been brought from Somerset in the time of Henry VIII. Apparently the monk who was entrusted with its safe-keeping became convinced that it was in danger from pirates, and so he concealed the treasure in a secret chamber and bricked it up from the inside, thus condemning himself to death in the process. A "luminous glow" is supposed to mark the site of the treasure.

Perhaps the best authenticated encounter with the phantom monk involved a hard-bitten workman called Arthur Gay. Years later, he told Roscoe Howells that one evening he was going round the greenhouse boilers when he clearly saw a monk in a black habit walking towards him. As he always did when greeting one of the brothers, he pulled his forelock and said "Good night brother." The shadowy monk did not even acknowledge him, but walked straight through the high garden wall and disappeared. Gay was intrigued to discover later on that there had once been a doorway in precisely that position and that it had later been bricked up.

Date: c 1925   *Source: Howells p 142; Bielski p 91*

7.5 The Ghost of Maesgwynne

Maesgwynne was a fine house not far from Llanboidy, in the Pembrokeshire-Carmarthenshire border country. The house was owned by the Powell family, whose members were renowned in the last century for their radical politics, their hospitality and their enthusiasm for the hunt.

In the late 1800's the estate passed to Miss Cardie Powell, while her stepmother, the widow of the late squire, undertook many projects on the rough land around the mansion. Before she died she planted conifers, rhododendrons, maples and exotic shrubs on the boggy infertile moorland and transformed it into a place of great beauty. She was particularly fond of one lovely spot outside the garden wall, where tall cypresses and Japanese maples were mirrored in the placid waters of an ornamental pond. After her death the trees grew to maturity, and many still remain.

Around 1910 a young farmer from the neighbourhood used to meet his sweetheart, who was a servant at the mansion, near the pond. He turned up one evening, by arrangement, but was a little early. As he waited for her in the shadows of the tall trees, he saw the figure of a short elderly lady emerge from a clump of golden yews. She was dressed all in black, with a white widow's cap, and she had a stick in her hand. He stared in amazement, for he instantly recognized old Mrs Powell, whom he had known well by sight during his boyhood. On realizing that he was watching the ghost of the late mistress of Maesgwynne, the poor fellow fell down in a faint; and unfortunately his sweetheart, when she turned up shortly afterwards, failed to notice him as he lay on the ground. Next morning they found him, still unconscious and suffering from the cold. He was carried home and, not surprisingly, developed rheumatic fever. Gradually he recovered, but it was a long time afterwards, during his convalescence, that he confided in his doctor and told the story of the ghostly encounter.

Date: c. 1910   *Source: Vaughan p 118*

Opposite: *a young farmer from the neighbourhood used to meet his sweetheart, who was a servant at the mansion, near the pond.*

7.6 The Saintly Lady of Rhos-y-Gilwen

Rhos-y-Gilwen, near Cilgerran, is one of a multitude of fine mansions once occupied by the gentry of the Teifi Valley. These houses were once the centres of social life in the valley; but they were also the places where commerce was conducted, and their estates saw many changes in agriculture and land management as the eighteenth and nineteenth centuries progressed. However, the good times could not last, and as the estates declined the sounds of music and laughter faded away. During the last century or so many of the fine houses (including Rhos-y-Gilwen) fell into a sad state of disrepair.

One day in 1990 the old mansion was gutted by fire, and it appeared that it would have to be abandoned. However, the shell of the building was bought by a small group of people who determined to bring it back to life. After years of hard work they replaced the roof, and gradually the restoration of the interior was taken in hand. During the early days of the work the residents were strangely moved on a number of occasions to play the Monteverdi "Vespers", and they began to believe that there was some sort of saintly presence in the building. In particular, they felt this presence on the main staircase and landing. David, one of the residents, had a number of experiences in which he saw the dim shape of a woman standing and watching him. On another occasion a woman resident was standing downstairs waiting for one of her children to come out of the downstairs toilet. She happened to glance into a large mirror in the passage and saw the reflected image of a woman standing behind her. She turned round, but there was nobody there.

There have been other sightings of the ghostly lady; but the consensus is that she is a serene and friendly guardian of the house. Some years ago David inquired in the village of Cilgerran as to the likely name of the saintly lady, and he was told by a very old resident of the village that her name was Mary. Apparently she had been a servant in the mansion many, many years ago. Furthermore, she had been a very religious person; and perhaps this goes some way to explaining the impulse which the residents of the house had in the early days after the fire to sing and play sacred music. The music of Monteverdi must have been familiar to the servants of the house in the eighteenth century.

Date: c 1990   *Source: word of mouth*

7.7 Ghostly Visit at Stepaside

In 1820 a certain Joshua Davies of Stepaside was greatly troubled by ghosts. As soon as he retired to bed he would be tormented by them, and he found it impossible to sleep. At last he went to consult a local witch, and she told him that when next he was visited by a ghost he

must get up and get dressed. Then, she said, the spirit would go outside, and he should follow. This he did. As predicted the nocturnal ghost went outside, crossed over to a hedge at the far end of the garden and motioned to Joshua to dig at a certain spot. He fetched a mattock from the shed and did as he was instructed. At length he came upon an earthenware pot. He opened it up and found inside a magnificent silver inkstand. He carried the treasure towards the house with him, and the ghost, which had been supervising the excavations, promptly disappeared.

But before he could reach his back door two hobgoblins appeared out of nowhere and chased after him, and he was struck several times by sharp stones which they threw at him. He fled indoors and shut the door with great relief. The hobgoblins did not trouble him any further, and after this uncomfortable episode he kept the inkstand in the house, suspecting that he would be very unwise ever to dispose of it. Sure enough he was never again troubled by ghosts and hobgoblins, and slept happily ever after.

Date : 1820   *Source : Meredith Morris p 97*

7.8 Three Ghostly Ladies of Llandawke

The simple little church of Llandawke is one of the oldest in West Wales, having escaped the attentions of the Victorian church restorers. It lies not far from the Pembrokeshire border in the rolling countryside inland of Pendine. It was founded in the thirteenth century by the Lady Margaret Marloes, daughter of a "noble foreigner" and wife of Sir Hugo Howel of Woodstock in Pembrokeshire. Not much is known about her, but she was referred to as a saint in the old days, possibly because of her good works as lady of the manor and possibly because of her devout and gentle nature. Her ghost is said to be one of three female ghosts which haunt the churchyard and nearby lanes.

The Lady Margaret is commemorated by a stone effigy which was once in the churchyard but which is now inside the church itself. The effigy shows a female figure in a long flowing robe and wimple, with slippers with peaked toes on her feet. Her hands are in an attitude of prayer. But the effigy is in three parts, and according to

tradition this is because she met a gruesome end. One day she was returning home after arranging details of the church building when she was attacked by robbers. They took all her possessions, killed her and cut her body into three parts. To commemorate her martyrdom her effigy was deliberately made in three separate pieces, and the church was dedicated to her as "St Margaret". A hundred years ago her ghost used to be seen in Llandawke Lane, at the place where she was killed.

The second of the Llandawke ghosts is that of a young lady murdered in the reign of Queen Elizabeth I, again in Llandawke Lane. According to legend, she was killed by her jealous lover, who buried her body at the side of the lane.

And the third of the local ghosts is that of a young bride who was married in Llandawke Church early in the nineteenth century. It is said that on her wedding day, following the marriage ceremony, she was killed close to the church by a jealous rival for her hand. The murderer threw her body into the pond behind the church, and then murdered the poor husband as well. His body was found outside the church door, but with no marks of violence upon it. Around 1820 local people used to see the ghost of the bride leaning over the gate close to the pond, particularly during the twilight hour. She was dressed in white, with a broad lilac sash tied with a large bow behind; and she wore a very large straw hat with lilac ribbons. As late as 1870 a farmer's wife used to see the ghost with the straw hat quite frequently as she passed Cwm Biddy on her way to milk the cows.

Date: c 1870   *Source: Curtis p 201*

7.9 The Parson's Home Brew

Tregynon Country Farmhouse Hotel is located on the southern side of the Gwaun Valley, which is famous for its tales of the supernatural. Tregynon was built in the 16th Century and was for many generations a farmhouse; and when the present proprietor moved in with his family in 1978 it was largely unmodified. The hotel is nowadays renowned for its warm hospitality and friendly atmosphere, and it certainly does not have a haunted feel about it.

However, there have been a number of strange incidents at Tregynon over the last few years. On a number of occasions guests have seen a shadowy figure in the passage of the old house, dressed in "old fashioned" clothes and carrying a small wooden cask either on his shoulder or under his arm. The proprietor has seen the figure himself on more than one occasion. Neither he nor the guests have been at all frightened by these encounters. Researches into the history of the house failed to provide any explanation of the ghostly inhabitant.

Then, however, the proprietor happened to mention his research task to one of the locals, who immediately said: "Oh yes -- that'll be the old parson." On being pressed further, she revealed that back in the early 1900's Tregynon was lived in by a reverend gentleman, who was amiable and well liked locally in spite of a little weakness. By all accounts he was rather too fond of alcoholic drinks, and was renowned for the quality of his home-brewed ale. He declared that the secret of his ale lay in the making of the casks; he disliked the large wooden barrels used by the local inn-keepers for their beer, and much preferred the small casks which could be easily carried about even when full.

The proprietor checked the story, and found that a jolly parson had indeed lived at Tregynon before the First World War.

Date: c 1985   *Source: word of mouth*

7.10   The UFOs at Nevern

Every now and then, small Pembrokeshire communities are awakened by strange and colourful sightings of unidentified flying objects. One such event -- or series of events -- occurred in 1992 in the village of Nevern.

It was a still and overcast autumnal evening when some of the locals who were heading down to the Trewern Arms for a quiet pint or two noticed strange flashing lights in the sky. The flashes were of green, red, blue and white light, and there was a sort of pulsing rhythm accompanied by a deep and barely-audible thumping sound. "Duw Duw!" said one of the men. "I never seen nothing like this before. It must be one of them UFOs from outer space." His friends agreed with him, and called the other locals who were already inside the inn. They all came out to look, and the experts agreed that they were indeed in the realm of the supernatural. They all agreed that they could see the flashing navigation lights and hear the pulsating warp generator that propelled the alien spacecraft faster than the speed of light. However, before any of them could get really frightened the lights disappeared and the sounds stopped, and they all concluded that the spacecraft had gone on its way.

For the rest of the evening the talk at the bar of the inn was of nothing else, and there was much speculation that the spacecraft might return. Sure enough, at about the same time next evening the strange lights appeared again for about 30 minutes, and even more people turned out to witness the phenomenon. The Trewern Arms did a roaring trade. Next night there was a repeat performance, and quite a crowd assembled on the bridge near the inn, pint glasses in their hands, to wonder at the mysteries of the universe. The word started to spread to far-off places like Newport and Eglwyswrw, but it appeared that the spacecraft was only seen in the Nevern area, and those who lived outside the close-knit community were understandably sceptical about the UFO story. The experts decided that there must be something special about Nevern to attract so much attention from alien visitors -- maybe it was the Celtic Cross or the bleeding yew trees in the Churchyard, or maybe there was something supernatural about the old pilgrim cross inscribed into the rock on the path to Newport?

But that was all they ever saw of the lights and heard of the pulsing motor, and many who came to Nevern on succeeding nights were disappointed to find nothing in particular going on. After a week or so the rumours of the UFOs reached the ears of a young man who lived in a cottage a couple of fields away from the Trewern Arms. He was rather intrigued, but then he remembered that on the three nights in question he had been out in the yard trying out the new laser lighting unit which he had just bought to go with his disc-jockey equipment. He had been banished by his mother to the yard because the lights were too bright to operate inside the cottage, and it so happened that on those three nights there had been a very low cloud-base, ideal for the low-level reflection of bright flashing lights.

He never had the heart to spoil a good story, and to this day there are those who frequent the bar of the Trewern Arms who will swear to you that there was, not very long ago. a strange visitation of aliens in the village of Nevern.

Date: 1992   *Source: word of mouth*

7.11   The Ferocious Housekeeper

A certain house in Newport was once occupied by Dr Davies, the local doctor, and his wife. The household was looked after by a very severe housekeeper; she ruled the place with such a rod of iron that the poor housemaid who worked under her went about her work in fear and trepidation, and it was reputed that even Dr Davies was scared of her. Shortly after Dr Davies died, the old housekeeper died also. The doctor's widow continued to live in the big house for some years, and during that time there was no evidence of ghostly activity.

Then a young local family moved into the house, and while renovation work was going on they lived in the attic (which was quite well appointed) for a while. This was where the old housekeeper had lived. But the parents became very concerned that the children would just not go into the bathroom; at bath-time in the evenings they more or less had to force them to go in through the door. There was clearly something there that frightened them. After a very short time they sold the property, and it was bought by a couple from Newport (Gwent). The wife was absolutely delighted with the big house at first; she told all the neighbours that it was just the place she had always wanted. In no time the new owners embarked upon a further renovation programme, with new electrical work, central heating, new carpeting and new decorations. The house was furnished in lavish style from top to bottom.

Then the wife disappeared. When the neighbours began to ask where she was, it appeared that nothing untoward had happened to her; but she had suddenly taken against the house, and had moved away from the area. Shortly after this the owners moved all their furniture out and the house was again put on the market. No reason was given, but rumours started to circulate that the big house was haunted.

While the house was on the market the owners asked a local man to undertake some further electrical work . The house was empty at the time, and the electrician worked on several occasions quite late into the evening. One evening he was invited to a nearby house for a meal after he had finished work; and he related to his hosts the strange experiences he had been having in the empty rooms and uncarpeted corridors. On a number of occasions he had felt that he was being watched, and more than once he felt the hair rising on the back of his neck. Once he had been so convinced that there was somebody there that he had called out and searched the house from top to bottom to find out who it was. He found nothing.

Neighbours who are old enough to remember old Dr Davies and his ferocious housekeeper are now convinced that the old lady has never really left the property. When the house is quiet and undisturbed, she rests in peace; but when there is noise and laughter, or when major alterations are going on, she gets extremely angry, and makes it her business to show her disapproval.......

Date: c 1990

Source: word of mouth

7.12 Strange Events at Bush House

The story of the haunting of Bush House in Pembroke is so well known that journalists and cameramen have even slept in the house in the hope of encountering either "the old-fashioned sporting gentleman and his phantom hounds" or "the white lady in her crinoline gown." Sightings of these two ghosts, and the hauntings experienced by workmen in the house, were recorded in Volume I (story 7.3).

There is a sequel. In recent years the house has been used as a home for elderly people. The eldest son of Mr David James works there as a care assistant. As a matter of routine, the local police call in now and then to check that all is well; and they have frequently reported that a light is on in one of the top floor rooms. On each occasion, a care assistant runs upstairs to the room in question, only to find the elderly residents fast asleep and the light off. At first the assistants assumed that one of the residents was playing games with them; but this has happened too often to be explained away as the work of a practical joker, and the strange feature of the case is that the room, and the passage outside, are always found by the care assistants to be bitterly cold, even when the central heating is full on. At other times the room and passage are at the same temperature as the rest of the house.

Date: 1992   *Source: David James*

7.13 The White Lady of Gosport House

Gosport House in Laugharne is the ancient residence of the Laugharne family -- one of the families which has figured frequently in Pembrokeshire history. Around 1830 a family of another name was living in the house. Two young brothers (but nobody else) used to see an apparition almost every night after they had gone to bed. A female ghost would pass across their window, her figure dressed in drapery and her hands covering her face. They thought she must be in deep distress, or else passing by in a state of deep devotion. The strange thing about this haunting was that the ghost passed in front of an upstairs window, namely the room above the drawing room and overlooking the sea. Many years later the two brothers related this to

Mary Curtis when she was writing her book on the antiquities of the Laugharne area. In the 1870s this "white lady" was still being observed at the house, once a year and always on 24th July. Presumably this must have been the anniversary of her death.

Date: 1830   *Source: Curtis p 12*

7.14 The Faceless Phantom of Cosheston

One night in January 1994 thirteen-year-old Gavin Roche was playing football with some friends in a Cosheston street, outside Pendine House. It was a cold, still night, and the children were playing beneath the street lights. Gavin took a break from the game, and as he stood on the pavement he glanced down the road. There he saw something he had never seen before, and has no wish to see again.

Suddenly, running out of the darkness, there came a tall faceless figure. "It was very tall," said Gavin afterwards, "like a skinny shadow, a silhouette, about 100 yards away. Within seconds it had covered the distance between us. I could see it, but I couldn't hear it, and there was nobody there. It was sort of floating towards me, but it was very fast. There was no wind that night, but its long hair was moving wildly as it sped past."

Gavin was the only one to see the phantom, but he became so scared that he shouted to his friends to run, and they all ran home as fast as their legs could carry them. After a while they decided to return to the street to investigate, and, if possible, to continue their game of football. But it was obvious that the phantom was still there, and this time a friend named Matthew Weidemann experienced a very strong sense of its presence. The boys ran away again, and this time stayed at home, trembling and feeling very scared. Gavin's mother Jacqueline quickly saw that he was very frightened indeed.

Afterwards one of the parents told the story to a local newspaper, and the publicity encouraged others to talk. It transpired that two of Gavin's other friends had also seen the faceless phantom a few weeks before. They had said nothing at the time because they were quite convinced that nobody would believe them.

Date: 1994   *Source: Western Telegraph 2.2.94*

7.15 The Haunted Bridge

It is said that Have-a-Care Bridge, between Haverfordwest and the Rhos, is haunted. The haunting there is unusual in that no ghosts are seen; but on dark and windy nights the unwary traveller is left in no doubt that there is something strange about the place.

The haunting begins with the distant sound of horses' hooves on the gravel road, in the direction of Haverfordwest. The galloping horses get closer and closer, and soon the sounds of creaking wheels and rattling harnesses are heard as well. It becomes clear that these are the sounds of a heavy coach pulled by four horses and travelling at great speed. As the phantom coach draws nearer to the bridge the listener hears the sound of a cracking whip above the clatter of the galloping hooves, and a phantom voice calls out "Whoa! Whoa!" with a note of increasing desperation. An invisible coach driver is attempting to slow the coach down, but the horses are out of control, and as the runaways reach the bridge there is a fearsome noise as the coach overturns and crashes on its side into the stonework of the bridge. In the cacophony of sound people scream and horses neigh, and then at last all becomes silent, save for the squeaking of two coach wheels as they spin freely on the top side of the stricken vehicle. The squeaking gets slower and slower, and then all is silent in the chill night air.

Little is known about the event which led to the haunting. However, there is a local tale about the de Rutzen family of Slebech Hall which gives us a clue. Apparently one winter's night four young people from the Hall (including two of the Baron's children who were in their early twenties) went to a Hunt Ball in Haverfordwest. They were strictly charged to return home by midnight. But they were late, and being afraid of the anger of their parents the young people urged the coach driver to go faster and faster, which was not very wise on a pitch-black winter's night. The horses at last ran out of control as they approached the dangerous bridge. All those on board the coach were killed in the accident.

Strangely, there is no record of such an event in the annals of Slebech Hall; but there are those alive today who have no doubt that the terrible accident actually happened.

Date: c 1820?   *Source: Mr Joe Leclair*

7.16 The Tenby Ghosts

Before the building of the new A478 road into Tenby there was an old road that ran further to the east, from New Hedges into the town. From this road a lane ran down towards the town reservoirs. There was once a gate here which was called "the spirit gate" by the children who played nearby. Once upon a time a young girl from the neighbourhood used to meet her lover at the gate, but then he betrayed her. So heartbroken was she that she jumped into one of the ponds and so took her own life. Her sad spirit continued to "keep tryst" at the gate for many years afterwards, and frightening the wits out of the local children.

In 1721-22 one Thomas Athoe was mayor of Tenby. In 1722 he travelled to Wiston Fair, and while there he became involved in a fierce quarrel about some cattle with a cousin of his called George Marchant. There was already bad blood between them because George had married a girl with whom Athoe's son had been passionately in love. So following the quarrel father and son decided to murder George Marchant. They laid in wait for him one day near the bridge over the Marsh Stream (Holloway Bridge) and killed him in a bloody and ferocious confrontation.

The murderers were caught and prosecuted, causing great excitement in the town since one of them was the mayor. They were found guilty of the horrible crime, and were hanged in London. But for over a century afterwards the ghosts of the three men still carried on their fierce and terrible fight under the old bridge, to the great annoyance of the people of Tenby.

Date: 1840   *Source: Francis Green Newscuttings, Vol 11 p 179*

7.17 The Ghost of St Florence

More than a century ago there was a troublesome ghost which haunted the parish of St Florence, not far from Tenby. The locals tried various methods of laying the ghost, without success, and then somebody said that experience had shown that only an Oxford man could lay this particular sort of ghost. Somebody said that the Rector of Tenby, the Rev Huntingdon, was such a man; and so it was decided that a delegation should go and visit him.

Some days later the delegation arrived at the church, and on being welcomed by the Rector they explained that they had come in the hope that he could exorcise a ghost from their parish. "But my dear friends," said the reverend gentleman, with a frown on his face, since he was not too keen on confronting ghosts. "Why on earth should you come to see me about this, when you have a perfectly splendid parson of your own in St Florence?"

"Well, Rector," replied the spokesman, "we do hear it said that only an Oxford man can get rid of this ol' ghost that's troublin' us. So we thought that you, bein' a very learned gentleman from college, must be jus' the man for the job."

Immediately a look of relief spread across the Rector's face. "I am afraid," he said, "that you have come to the wrong place, for I am a Cambridge man through and through!"

Greatly discouraged, the deputation trudged back to St Florence, which is probably still troubled by the ghost to this day.

Date: c 1880

Sources: Bielski, 1979

7.18 The Ghostly Pirate Ship

On a dark midwinter afternoon in about 1558, in the reign of Queen Elizabeth the First, the people of Tenby saw a strange vessel sweeping across Carmarthen Bay. Driven by storm-force winds and mighty waves from the east, it was obviously out of control, with broken masts and spars, and shredded sails. As it came closer and closer to the shore, the people could see that it was unmanned, but there were strange lights and "spirit-forms" moving about on the deck, and word soon spread that this was a phantom ship, or at least a solid ship populated by phantoms.

As darkness fell,. the people could just make out the shape of the ship close inshore as she foundered upon a sand-bank close to the North Beach. Throughout the pitch-black night the people heard wailing and other strange ghostly sounds, as a result of which those living close to the beach had very little sleep. At first light the storm had calmed, and the townspeople went down to the shore to search

for the shipwreck. But there was not a trace of the ghostly vessel --
no timbers or rigging, no barrels, no strips of sail, no flotsam or jetsam
of any sort. But upon the sand lay a man dressed in strange clothes,
half drowned and unconscious. The people pulled him clear of the
waves and managed to revive him, and for a few days he stayed in
the town as he was nursed back to health. But he was a strange
fellow, unwilling to talk about himself or even to give his name to
those who would be his friends, and at last he moved out to live on
the rocks of St Catherine's Island, which was cut off from the town
with every high tide.

One day a local shepherd heard about the sailor's hermit-like
existence on the island, and went across at low tide with some food
and clothes. The man was grateful, and over the days and weeks that
followed the shepherd went across to bring him food whenever he
came in to Tenby to visit the town market. The sailor seemed to
spend his time sitting on a crag gazing out to sea, with the seabirds
wheeling about him. On each visit the shepherd begged the sailor to
abandon his bleak and joyless existence and to go home with him, but
the stranger always refused courteously.

Then at last, one stormy day when the waves were crashing
against the seaward side of the little island, the stranger opened his
heart to the shepherd. In a torrent of words he talked of his former
life as a pirate, and he related how, in a fit of jealousy, he had
murdered the woman who loved him most. He said that all his
comrades had perished on his ship, which was then manned by
ghosts while driven by the storm onto the sands of the town's North
Beach. At times, he said, as he sat upon the cliffs facing out to sea,
sea maidens came and beckoned to him, calling out that his girl was
happy and at rest.

Suddenly, as a great foam-crested wave rolled in towards the
cliff where the two men were sitting, the pirate stood up in a highly
agitated state. He pointed at the wave and shouted "I come. I come.
Receive me, blest spirits!" And before the shepherd could stop him he
leaped from the clifftop into the surging foam and was immediately
lost to view. The horrified shepherd could do nothing, and returned
to the mainland alone. The pirate's body was never found.

Date: c 1558   *Source: Bielski, 1979; Mason, 1858*

7.19 The Ghostly Monks of St Buttock

Not far from the Elf-Murco Refinery (originally built and operated by Amoco) there is a fine mansion which has a long and fascinating history. It was built on the site of St Buttock's Chapel, named after a Celtic saint named Buttock or Buddock. The chapel was used as a place of worship by the monks of Pill Priory, which was less than a mile away.

The old chapel was in ruins by the late Middle Ages, and the first mansion was built on the site during the 1500's. It was rebuilt in 1807 as a stately and elegant home; and since the original name was not suitable for use in the most refined of circles, the mansion was re-named St Botolph's. When Amoco was involved in the construction of the nearby refinery the company bought the house and grounds for use as an office and residence for key workers.

One night a worker was woken up by a strange sound which at first he could not identify; then, when he was fully awake, he realised that the sound was that of a group of monks chanting and praying. Eventually the sound disappeared and the man went back to sleep. Nobody believed him when he related this to his colleagues in the morning; and indeed neither he nor anybody else at the time was aware that the site was once used as a place of worship by the monks of Pill Priory.

So far as we know, this is the only recorded instance of a ghostly haunting by monks in the mansion. However, there is another resident ghost which began to appear after the mansion was bought and converted into luxury flats by Mr and Mrs Beer. The ghost is female, and appears occasionally on the main staircase, dressed in white. She is perfectly harmless and friendly, and some of her visitations are remembered by Mrs Merryl Lloyd, who was brought up in the mansion.

Date: 1984   *Source: W. Tel. press cutting 18.07.84*

7.20   The Bwcci Bal at Cilgerran

The Bwcci Bal was a horrible hobgoblin that lived in the woods near Cilgerran. It was of vast size, and would frighten the wits out of all those who encountered it. In other parts of Pembrokeshire this creature would have been called a *Gwyllgi* or Hound of Hell -- but it was apparently more like a gigantic demon with a man-like form.

The road was overlooked by dark and gloomy woods populated by ancient oaks and soot-black shadows.

Page 114

On 21st August 1850 a farmer was returning home from Ffair Laurens (St Lawrence Fair) in Cilgerran, having sold all his cattle and having enjoyed a jolly evening with his friends and neighbours. He had to walk alone along the road at Glanpwllafon, which is overlooked by dark and gloomy woods populated by ancient oaks and soot-black shadows.

Suddenly he heard rapid and heavy footsteps behind him, and assuming that somebody was wanting to pass him, he stepped aside. But nobody passed, and the footsteps fell silent. A little mystified and afraid, he continued on his way through the dark shadows, and heard heavy footsteps behind him again. He stopped, but again there was only silence and the faint sighing of the wind in the trees.

Now he was thoroughly alarmed, and walked as fast as he could. But as he walked faster, so did the heavy footsteps behind him. At last he dared to look over his shoulder, and he saw a huge shadowy form beneath the trees not far behind him. He broke into a run and sped towards the safety of a little cottage that he knew was not far ahead - but even as he ran he could hear the steady thump of the gigantic feet hitting the roadway behind him.

At last he reached the safety of the cottage and banged on the door, but as soon as he arrived the Bwcci Bal disappeared. When he had recovered, the man showed the cottager the great splashes of mud on his back, which he swore had been thrown up from the muddy lane by the monster's feet. This tale was told to Mr F L Lowther of Milford, when he was a child, by a family maid. The man who was chased by the Bwcci Bal was her uncle.

Date: c 1850?   *Source: Press Cuttings 28, p 105*

7.21 Ghostly Events in the Castle Inn

There is a long tradition of hauntings in the Castle Inn in Narberth. Perhaps this is not surprising, since the old ruined castle is not far away, and castles are almost always inhabited by ghosts. Maybe the castle ghosts move into nearby inns where conditions are much warmer and a lot less draughty?

In 1982 Mr and Mrs Mel Taylor took over the inn and experienced a number of strange incidents, which confirmed in their minds tales about the building being haunted. A previous landlady had seen a ghostly figure dressed in a monk's habit, and in the early 1980s doors would suddenly open or close, lights would be turned off and on, and sometimes the beer coolers would be turned off in the middle of the night. One evening a neighbour, Mr Hughie John, saw a "tall man in a waistcoat" standing next to Mrs Mary Tyler behind the bar. She was quite unaware of the presence of anybody.

The most bizarre incidents occurred when a young couple were occupying a room on the second floor. In the middle of the night the young man, named Adam, got up to visit the bathroom. He returned to bed and was half asleep when the door burst open, even though it had been fastened on a latch. Then he saw his cigarettes, matches and car keys suddenly flip over as they lay on top of the record player at the bedside. Next day the lights went out of their own accord while he was in the bathroom.

Mr and Mrs Tyler moved out of the inn after 3 months, but they claimed that the ghosts were not at all troublesome, and that family reasons lay behind the move.

Date: 1982   *Source: W. Tel. 5.9.84*

A bright moon was hidden intermittently behind scudding black clouds. There was half a gale blowing, but the sea sparkled.....

7.22 The Great White Whale at Strumble Head

Once upon a very long time ago, in 1954, a local man from Pencaer was making his way home along the Coast Path near Strumble Head. Let us call him Billy Evans. It was very late at night, and a bright moon was hidden intermittently behind scudding black clouds. There was half a gale blowing, but the sea sparkled and there was just enough light to see where the path was located along the cliff edge.

Billy had had quite a few too many, for he had been trying out some of his neighbour's lethal home brew (one of a series of wonderful concoctions made with bottles, pipes and tubes, and reputed to be just right for cleaning knives, dipping sheep and clearing blocked drains). He was walking home along the coast path so that he might breathe in a bit of salt air and clear his head – but also because he wanted to avoid passing the home of a notorious spinster who would certainly hear his footsteps on the road outside her window. She was a most formidable woman, whose face had been known to stop a clock, whose voice had turned milk sour, and whose gaze could freeze the blood of brave men at a range of fifty yards. She had threatened to curse Billy's soul to hell and damnation next time she saw him drunk – so he thought it prudent, on this particular night, to keep well clear of her cottage.

As Billy rounded the headland near the light-house his blood froze, for there, close inshore, was a gigantic white whale driven by the waves and approaching at a rate of knots in the moonlight. It was heading straight for him. Billy knew in an instant that this was really the Devil come to take him, but he was not a man to give up easily, and so he sobered up pretty smartly and headed inland as fast as his legs would carry him. He did not stop running until he had reached the front door of a lonely farmhouse. There he hammered on the door until the farmer woke up and let him in; and then he fell on his knees, told the Good Samaritan of his vision, and swore never to touch another drop of Elwyn's home brew.

According to the local historians of the neighbourhood, Billy has kept his word. He joined a Temperance Society, started going to chapel every Sunday, and generally became a pillar of society. The only after-effect of the ghostly incident on his health was that he broke out in a cold sweat every time he heard Vera Lynn singing "Whale meat again" ....

By the way, this may or may not be relevant, but in 1954 they were filming "Moby Dick" in Fishguard. One day, during filming in the harbour, a gale sprang up which caused the great white whale's tow-rope to snap. The monster, 70 feet long, with a steel frame and weighing 12 tonnes, drifted out to sea and all attempts to recover it were unsuccessful. It was declared a hazard to shipping, but in spite of a search by land, sea and air it was completely lost.

Date: 1954   *Source: Keith Worthing, County Echo*

7.23   The Hauntings at Merlin's Bridge

On Sunday 19 October 1890 Mr JW Phillips, a solicitor of Haverfordwest, was walking home following a visit to friends at Little Milford. Soon he was approaching the outskirts of the village of Merlin's Bridge. He was passing an old-fashioned house called Woodbine, at about 10.20 pm, when he saw a strange animal gliding across the road just in front of him. It was about the size of a fox, but whitish in colour. He was certain it wasn't a fox; the strange animal made no noise at all, but simply glided across the road, apparently oblivious to his presence. It then disappeared.

Some days later, on a cloudy moonlit night, Mr Phillips was passing the same spot, when he saw a very large black dog. At least, he thought at first that it must be a dog. It was as big as a St Bernard's, and was standing with its front feet on a pile of stones. On closer examination the creature proved not to be a dog at all, for it had the head of a goat, with horns. While Mr Phillips watched, it moved to the entrance of the lane and then leaped over a pile of timber into a patch of brambles, but in spite of its large bulk there was no noise at all.

Later, on November 10th, Mr Phillips was again walking home from Little Milford alone, around 10 pm. He heard an intense noise as soon as he left the house. It sounded like the flapping wings of a very large bird, sometimes in front, sometimes behind, sometimes above and very close to his head. The noise continued all the way past Lower Freystrop, and followed him as he walked down into a hollow called Culvert Bridge. There he met two strange and ghostly men who passed him without a word. Neither were they speaking to each other. Strangely, the noise of the "wings" stopped as soon as the men passed.

Mr Phillips continued towards GWR Bridge near Merlin's Bridge. There he heard the flapping noise again. It got louder and louder and sounded like a panting noise followed by a deep-throated roar. At this point he became quite alarmed. He stopped and stood in a defensive posture with his stick raised, waiting for an attack from some animal. Then he heard an almighty crash in the bushes on top of the fence and saw a huge black creature in the darkness leaping down into the road. It then rushed off up the hill towards Woodbine.

Mr Phillips walked many more times between Haverfordwest and Little Milford by the same route, but never again experienced these strange ghostly phenomena.   But in 1920 he recorded that five other people had seen a large black creature ("between a dog and a calf") on the Pembroke Ferry Road about 2 miles from Haverfordwest. Merlin's Bridge people said that there was "fear" on that part of the road, and would not pass it alone at night.

Date: 1890   *Source: Western Telegraph, Almanac 1937*

7.24 Ghostly Funeral in Haverfordwest

In September 1978, 13-year old Jane Evans of Hawthorn Rise was going off to bed and went to the window to draw her bedroom curtains. She glanced outside as she did so, and saw down below, very clearly, in the City Road cemetery, several people standing around a grave. She screamed and fell sobbing onto her bed. Mr and Mrs Evans rushed upstairs to see what the matter was. Jane told them she had seen people in the cemetary. Mrs Evans looked out, and saw a group of ghostly figures and the grave of her husband's grandparents. Most of the people were bending down over the grave, but one very tall man was standing up. She saw him very plainly, dressed in black clothing and with a high stiff collar and large top hat. "He looked very much like an old-fashioned minister or undertaker", said Mrs Evans. Her husband thought that somebody must be playing some sort of prank, so went to the cemetery to investigate. There was no sign of anybody and no traces of foot marks on the grass. The family members were quite convinced that they had witnessed a ghostly funeral "replay" involving one of Mr Evans's grandparents.

Date: 1978   *Source: Haverfordwest Newscuttings, Vol 1, p 76*

PEMBROKESHIRE
FOLK TALES

FOLK
HEROES
GREAT
AND
SMALL

8.1   Strange Men on the Mountain

Mr and Mrs Salmon of Brynderi were fast asleep in their beds very early on the morning of Sunday 19th August 1934 when they were awoken by a thunderous knocking on their front door. It took them some minutes to get over the shock. At first they did not believe their ears, for in their remote cottage on the slopes of Carningli, above Newport, they were not used to having visitors even in the daylight hours. Furthermore, it was a filthy night, as black as the grave, with storm-force winds blowing in from the sea, accompanied by low cloud and driving rain. Even if it had been light, visibility would not have been more than a few yards.

Again the knocking came louder and more persistent than before, and the old couple saw that somebody was shining a flashlight through their window. At last Mr Salmon plucked up enough courage to go downstairs and go to his locked and bolted front door. Once there he shouted (in Welsh) "What do you want?" A man's voice shouted something in reply, but the wind and the rain drowned out the words. Then another voice, sounding very foreign, also shouted at him. Mr Salmon, being a cautious sort of fellow, assumed that he was dealing either with criminals or with a couple of tramps who wanted shelter from the storm. He refused to open the door and shouted (again in Welsh) "Clear off! Go and find yourselves a bed somewhere else. How dare you knock on my door at 4 o'clock on a Sunday morning when all good folks are fast asleep?"

The strange voices pleaded and the knocking continued for a while, but when it became clear that the cottage was not inhabited by a Good Samaritan the strange visitors eventually went away, leaving Mr Salmon to return to his warm, dry bed.

One of the two men at the front door of Brynderi on that foul night was quite badly injured. Both were very lucky to be alive. They were Capt. George Pond, an American pilot, and Lt. Casare Sabelli, an Italian airman who was his co-pilot and navigator. They were flying from Rome to Dublin, en route for New York, having made the journey in the opposite direction in May 1934. They had hoped that theirs would be a record-breaking journey, and their aircraft, the **Leonardo Da Vinci**, was very modern for its time, being equipped with the latest scientific instruments. It carried gifts and a goodwill message from the Italian leader Benito Mussolini.

However, neither the instruments nor the support of Mussolini could keep the aircraft in the air over Cardigan Bay on that fateful night, for after a hitherto trouble-free flight it encountered heavy mist, high winds and driving rain which made navigation impossible. After flying blind over the sea for more than one hour Capt Pond decided to return to Pembrokeshire in the hope of making an emergency landing. They crossed the coast near the Strumble Head light, flew on and then decided to circle at an altitude of 1200 feet while they waited for an improvement in the weather and for the light of dawn. However, with fuel supplies running low and with a faulty altimeter the aircraft lost height, and Pond and Sabelli were horrified when the aircraft hit something very solid when flying at about 80 mph. It took off again, but, as the men braced themselves for the inevitable, it ploughed into a patch of gorse bushes and after about 40 yards hit a rock. It turned a complete somersault and came to rest upside-down.

Having ascertained that neither of them had broken any bones, the men managed to release themselves from their safety-harnesses, and then they hurried clear of the wreck, afraid that it would catch fire. The driving rain reduced the risk to some degree, and after a few minutes, the two airmen, in a deep state of shock, returned to the aeroplane to collect their thoughts. They had no idea where they were. But they were quickly soaked to the skin by the rain, and they decided that they had better head down-hill in the hope of finding shelter. They took a flashlight from the wreck and headed off into the pitch-black night. After about half a mile they came to the lonely cottage where they encountered Mr Salmon's frosty welcome.

Disturbed by the apparent hostility of the locals, Pond and Sabelli decided not to walk any further until they had some daylight to guide them. So they returned to the aircraft, where they found enough shelter from the wind and rain to sleep for a while. Then, at dawn, they set off again to find help. This time they came to Blaenffynnon Farm, where they found three generations of the family of Mr and Mrs Tom John, together with some visitors from Llanelli. They were immediately taken in and given a warm welcome, a hot meal and some dry clothes, and the family listened in fascination as Capt Pond recounted the story of their adventure.

The two aviators were later taken to Newport and provided with accommodation in the Commercial Hotel. Dr Havard, the local JP and GP, examined the men and found extensive cuts and bruising; but Capt Pond was in great pain from a damaged rib, and he was taken to Cardigan hospital for an X-ray examination.

The remains of the **Leonardo Da Vinci** immediately became something of a local attraction, and as news of the Newport incident spread through the community, hundreds of people climbed onto the flanks of Carningli to see the wreck. (In fact, many local people had heard the plane flying overhead, very low, shortly before the crash.) People climbed all over the aircraft, and many photographs were taken. So concerned was Capt Pond at the potential damage to the aircraft, and at the prospect of petty pilfering, that two local men, Messrs Wilde and Humphries, were appointed to keep watch. Later the aircraft was placed in the care of a government department in Fishguard, and after ascertaining that it was too badly damaged to be repaired, the aircraft was dismantled, crated and taken to London for eventual dispatch by sea to America.

The work on the aircraft took several weeks, and during this time the two aviators became local celebrities. On the day of the crash they were invited to dinner by the Lady Marcher of Cemais in Newport Castle, and on the following night they were entertained by Dr Havard and his wife. They were entertained by a folk dance group, and later a dance was held in their honour in the Memorial Hall. The band on that occasion was the West Cambrian Syncopators, of which Mr Jack Holt of Prendergast, Haverfordwest, was the drummer. When the aviators finally said farewell to Newport in December 1934, the town had forged a firm and friendly link with them, more than making up for the initial hostile response of the locals on the night of the crash.

Date: 1934   *Source: John Evans, Pembs Magazine, Dec 1984*

8.2 Callican and the Donkeys

One of the great characters of Solva around 1880 was Edward Callican (or Callaghan). He was a carter who used to fetch and deliver small loads for local people. Mostly his journeys would be made without a cart - but donkeys were common in the Solva area and he would often borrow donkeys for some of his "delivery runs". He used to travel to Nolton once a fortnight to fetch culm from the collieries. If you ordered a sack of culm (which was much cheaper than the graded anthracite) Callican would fetch it for you - and if you had a donkey he would take it and use it as the beast of burden. Having assembled his order, he would set off early in the morning with a "train" of up to 20 donkeys following him, and he would return to Solva in the evening with each animal bearing a full sack. The charge was one penny per sack if you provided the donkey, and two pence otherwise. The sight of Callican and his "donkey train" filing along the coast track and along the edge of the Newgale storm beach was one of the most enduring sights remembered by elderly locals who were still alive around the time of the 2nd World War.

Callican was also one of the last people in Pembrokeshire to celebrate "Hen Dydd Galan" or the Old New Year (13th January) by carrying around a little iron cage or lantern. In the old days this would have been called a "wren house", and it would have contained a live cutty wren. In South Pembrokeshire the parading of the wren house around the community would have taken place shortly after Christmas, on Boxing Day or St Stephen's Day. For his wren house Callican used a lantern containing a small figure covered with bird's feathers. As an old man, he would wander around Solva with his stick and his lantern, bent double with arthritis and singing in a thin quavering voice verses (which were unintelligible to most people) about Drew Fach or Jenny Wren. The origins of the custom supposedly go back to pre-Christian times, when the spirit of Life was called back from the under-world at the beginning of the New Year when the days were beginning to lengthen.

Date: c. 1880?   *Source: Press Cuttings vol 28, p 123*

8.3 How Hemmy saved the Bacon

One fine summer's day a cottager (let us call him Dafydd) was walking his very large pig from Caerfarchell to the next hamlet, where it was destined for an unpleasant encounter with a butcher's knife. Dafydd was actually rather fond of the pig, which was an amiable creature, but was taking it for slaughter at the insistence of his wife who was more interested in food supplies than pets.

On the way Dafydd passed Tresais Farm, where Evan and Elizabeth John lived. He thought he would stop for a quick chat, and when he saw Hemmy, the youngest daughter, sitting on the hedge plaiting daisies, he called out: "Hemmy, will you keep an eye on my pig while I pop in to have a little chat with your parents? Here's a penny for you." Hemmy was delighted with her penny, and promised to keep an eye on the pig. Then she went and played happily on the edge of the pond.

Then Hemmy went and played happily on the edge of the pond......

So Dafydd went inside the farmhouse, where he was soon chatting nineteen to the dozen with Evan and Elizabeth, and tucking into slices of freshly baked bread with butter and jam. It was a good hour before he emerged, replete, into the farmyard; and when he looked around for his beloved pig he could see no sign of it. "Hemmy, where's my pig?" he asked. With tears in her eyes the little girl pointed into the distance, where the pig was happily snuffling about on the far side of the moor. All four of them set off in hot pursuit, scrambling across hedges and ditches and getting thoroughly wet and dirty as they splashed through pools and boggy patches. Puffing and panting, they at last reached the pig and made a dive for it. But although it was a very large and cumbersome beast, it was too quick for them, and it led them a merry dance around the edges of the moor. At last Dafydd went and borrowed a rope, and after further exciting adventures they managed to get the rope around the pig's middle and brought it under control.

As they led the pig back to Tresais Hemmy's father began to let off steam, and scolded the little girl for stupidly letting the pig wander off. With tears in her eyes, Hemmy admitted that she had not been paying attention to the pig, and she offered her penny back to Dafydd. "No, no," said Dafydd. "You keep the penny, bach. It's yours, for we haven't actually lost the pig, have we?"

By this time it was far too late for Dafydd to continue on his journey to the butcher, so he took his leave of the family and headed for home with the pig on the end of its rope. As it passed her on its way down the lane, Hemmy was quite sure that the pig gave her a wink. Dafydd never did manage to get the pig to the butcher, and according to local historians it lived to a ripe old age.

Date: 1925   *Source: Judith Di-Sandolo*

8.4 Value for Money

Dai and Iorwerth Rhys were bachelor brothers running a small farm up in the hills near Brynberian, with a bit of contracting work and dealing on the side. One of their sidelines was the collection and disposal of fallen animals.

One sad day, Iorwerth fell under a tractor and was killed. After making the necessary arrangements for the funeral, Dai thought he had better let the world know, so he rang the "Western Telegraph" office in Haverfordwest.

"I want to put a Death Notice in the paper," he said. "How much?"

"Certainly, sir," said the young lady. "Minimum nine words, and the cost is £5. What do you wish to say?"

"Put this: Iorwerth Rhys is dead."

"Very well," said the girl. "But you can have another five words for the same price."

Dai thought for a moment, and then, being a consummate businessman, he said: "You can add this: We also buy dead cows."

Date: 1992   *Source: word of mouth*

8.5 The Boss Knows Best

Young Gideon lived on a little farm near Mathry. One day he went to his father and said: "Dad, I'm thinkin' of gettin' married to that Blodwen from Croesgoch. But she wants to be the boss and so do I. Who should be the boss, me or my wife?"

Gideon's father smiled enigmatically and said: "There's a lesson for ye to learn, son. Take the hens from the chicken-run and load them into a box on the cart. Take two of the horses to pull the cart, and then go off to St David's on the back road. Stop whenever ye find a man and a wife dwellin' together, and enquire as to who is the boss of the household. Wherever ye find a woman in charge, leave a hen. If ye come to a place where the husband is in control, leave a horse. If ye come back home without the hens but still with the horses and the cart, ye can have them as a weddin' present."

So off Gideon went on his journey of discovery. One by one he disposed of the hens, until there was only one left. He called at a small farm near Abereiddi, and on meeting the husband made the usual enquiry. "I'm the boss o' this place, that's for sure", said the man. "Ain't that right, Lizzy?" "Right you are," said Lizzy. "Tis you, sure enough, husband bach, that decides everythin' in this house."

"Take whichever horse you like", said Gideon.

"I'll take the bay," said the husband. But the wife did not like the look of the bay and whispered in her husband's ear. Then he said: "On second thoughts, all things considered, I'll take the grey."

"Oh no you won't," retorted Gideon. "You take the hen. I keep the horses, and Blodwen takes charge."

Date: c 1920   *Source: traditional*

8.6 Georgie's Trip to Market

In the old days it used to be said (by people who should have known better) that the people of Marloes were a bit slow on the up-take. They were referred to all over Pembrokeshire as "Marloes gulls", maybe because gull's eggs were a part of their diet. There are many famous stories about Marloes folk, and this is one of them.

Billy was out one Friday morning in his garden, dressed up in his oilskins since it was pouring with rain. He was watering his roses with a watering-can. As he worked he saw his friend Georgie going past, with a wheelbarrow half-full of onions. Later on in the day, just as it was getting dark, he saw Georgie coming back again, still pushing his wheelbarrow with the onions. "Where'st tha bin?" shouted Billy.

"It's Harfat market tomorrow," replied Georgie. "Tis a devil of a long way to go with all me onions to sell, so I thought to meself I'd go halfway today, so as to make the journey that much quicker tomorrow." "So why hast tha come back again after goin' all that way?"

"I has to get a good night's rest in me own bed so as to have the strength for the rest of the journey. An' can't tha see, tha daft bugger, that me barra is only half-full of onions? I had to come back whatever, to fetch the other half."

Date: c 1960   *Source: word of mouth*

8.7 Not Actually Needed

Gerald James had a little general store in Haverfordwest before the First World War. One Friday in the year 1910 he was behind his counter when a very scruffy little boy came in, looking somewhat ill at ease. Gerald had never seen him before. "What can I do for you, young man?" he asked. "Please sir, my mam says please to sell me a roll of toilet paper."

Gerald took down a roll from the shelf and said "That will be threepence, please." The boy paid over the money, took the toilet roll and scuttled out of the shop.

First thing on Monday morning the little boy was back again, carrying the toilet roll under his arm and carrying a letter in his hand. "Please sir," he explained, "my mam says please to read the letter." Gerald opened it up and read as follows:

> "Dear Sir, Billy is taking the roll of toilet paper back to you, and please to pay him the money back what he paid you. We will not be needing the toilet roll. Our visitors never came."

Date: 1910   *Source: word of mouth*

8.8 A Nice Lie In

Dicky and Nellie were a happily married old couple from Carew, who were somewhat confused during the Second World War while the air raids were going on over the area. Instructions came down from on high that all houses had to fit blinds or curtains so as to achieve a total blackout, and a neighbour called Jeb kindly helped the old couple to complete the job.

Three days later Jeb and the other neighbours became seriously worried since they had not seen the old couple since the blackout was installed. They hammered on the front door, and eventually a bleary-eyed Dicky came to the door in his pyjamas. "That's a relief to see you, Dicky," said Jeb. "We thought you was both dead!" "Why no, boy," replied Dicky. "In bed we are, waitin' for it to get light!"

Date: 1941   *Source: word of mouth*

8.9 The Cancer Healers of Cardigan

Daniel and John Evans were brothers who lived at Pen-y-banc, a smallholding located between Ferwig and Cardigan. The holding was not large enough to support both of them, but they were also shipwrights who earned an intermittent income from working on the little shipbuilding yards along the Teifi estuary. They were both good musicians and were deeply religious men, faithful in their attendance of Tabernacle Chapel in Cardigan. They both had an interest in medicinal plants, and in their local area they began to develop a

reputation for the healing of skin complaints through the use of a herbal medicinal oil. According to the locals, some of their plants were gathered during the day, and others strictly under cover of darkness. By 1906, by which time John was already 69 years old, their reputation was so firmly established that they were being referred to as "The Cancer Healers of Cardigan". They were openly taking on cases of skin cancer which were beyond the abilities of conventional doctors to cure. There is no doubt that many very sick people were completely cured by these simple and pious men.

In 1906 the novelist Allen Raine wrote in her diary : "Poor Mrs Davies the Mill is being treated for cancer by the herbal doctors in Cardigan. I hope they won't hasten her end." Two months later she wrote: "Went down to Gwalia Mill to see poor Mrs Davies and found Tobit Evans and his wife there. Poor Mrs Davies wonderfully rid of the lump on her face ...... James Evans, Dyffryn Saith, has been cured too by these herbalists."

By 1907, as a result of publicity in the national newspapers, the fame of the Evans brothers had spread all over Britain, and sad disfigured cancer sufferers flocked into Cardigan in search of a cure. There were so many of them that the locals began to resent their presence in the town's parks and gardens, and in the hotels and guest-houses. Many locals were frightened that the skin cancer might be contagious, and they genuinely feared an epidemic. Towards the end of the year news of the cure had spread all over the world, and sufferers came to Cardigan from America and Canada, France, Germany, Egypt, South Africa and even Japan.

The secret of the treatment was a herbal oil, the recipe for which was a closely guarded secret. The brothers, who were normally both involved in the diagnosis and treatment of patients, claimed that the oil acted to kill cancerous growths that had spread "tentacles" into the body of the patient. They explained that as the growth died it released its grip and finally fell away, leaving just healthy tissue behind. This is exactly what happened, in the testimony of many patients.

The brothers kept their secret oil in small bottles, and with very little regard for hygiene a brush would be dipped into the bottle and the oil applied to the cancerous growth. The brushes were not washed between treatments, and often the brothers would squeeze the last drops of oil from the brush back into the bottle after seeing one patient and before calling the next. When patients complained about their lack of hygiene they asked them to bring their own brushes, but still they sqeezed the last drops of oil back into the bottle, and then washed the brush before giving it back to the patient. The oil was clearly extremely valuable and difficult to make; and the brothers were insistent that nobody else was going to take away a sample of it -- on a brush or in any other way -- which might enable any rivals to undertake a scientific analysis of its contents.

Inevitably, the medical establishment began to take a keen interest in the Evans brothers and their secret oil. A number of doctors travelled to Cardigan to investigate their treatment methods; some departed full of admiration, while others denounced the brothers as quacks. A storm raged in the medical press and in the newspapers, and the British Medical Association and the Cancer Research Committee were heavily criticised for their reluctance to take the "Cardigan Cancer Cure" seriously. In a way the brothers were the victims of their own success and victims of the times in which they lived; for such was their fame that people suffering from other forms of cancer -- which could not possibly be cured with their herbal skin remedy -- began to turn up and seek the cures which the medical

People suffering from other forms of cancer -- which could not possibly be cured with their herbal skin remedy -- began to turn up and seek help.

science of the day could not give them. Sometimes, against their better judgement, the brothers agreed to try and help. Inevitably, many of these new patients died in Cardigan, and it is this fact above all others that led to an increasingly cynical attack by the medical establishment. No proper medical study of the efficacy of the secret oil was ever undertaken, but the BMA and the CRC sent one Walter Hadwen MD to do a vicious hatchet job on the brothers, and in a long newspaper article published in August 1907 he effectively destroyed their reputations in the world at large.

The brothers continued to work from their little surgery in Pendre, Cardigan, in the years that followed. They did not vary their treatment method very much, and continued to treat all who needed help, charging for their services at a level the patient could afford, and for the poorest charging no fees at all. The brothers refused substantial sums of money for their recipe, and they were reputed to have been offered in excess of £25,000 on one occasion and over £45,000 by a healed patient from the United States.

From about 1910 onwards the brothers' healing work was greatly reduced. John was in failing health, and it may be that a sales restriction on arsenic affected their ability to make up their potion. (It probably contained chloride of zinc, arsenic and other substances obtained from the local chemist, in addition to herbs collected locally.) John Evans died in 1913 , and Daniel in 1919.

The recipe for the healing oil did not die with the the brothers. It was left in the safe hands of David Rees Evans, who was John's eldest son, and after the First World War he used it frequently in the course of his profession as a medical herbalist. The use of the oil led him eventually into deep trouble, but that is another story...........

Date: 1907   *Source: Jones and Jones, 1993*

8.10 Isaiah and the Beautiful Trout

In the 1920s and 1930s the Rev Isaiah Jenkins was a memorable Rector of St Nicholas. His great loves were his little church, his congregation, vegetable growing, shooting and fishing. There are many stories about his prowess as a huntsman, but one particularly noteworthy episode relates to his love of trout fishing.

The Squire's pond in St Nicholas became redundant in the inter-war years with the closure of the water-driven corn mill which had depended upon it for its water supply. In 1929 the Squire decided to drain it and clean it, and then to stock it with rainbow trout. The trout grew to be monsters, and people marvelled at the way in which they leaped out of the water of a summer's evening to catch the swarming midges. The Squire made it quite clear to all and sundry that the fishing in the pond was strictly a private affair, and although many local fishermen cast envious eyes at its teeming trout there was apparently no poaching.

Then one evening, when the whole village was attending a nearby Fair and the Squire's house was also empty, a furtive figure in a dark coat made his way, via a lengthy detour across the fields, to the Squire's pond. It was the Rector, intent upon a spot of illicit trout fishing. Once there, he climbed the iron ladder up the pond bank, got out his equipment, and set to work with the underarm fling of the trout poacher. He was actually quite proficient, and had clearly used this technique before. Within half an hour there were twelve fat trout in his canvas bag. Then, exceedingly content with his day's work, he stood up, dismantled his rod and turned to leave the scene of the crime. But then, without warning, the bank gave way under him, and he slid in very undignified fashion into the water. It was so deep that he could just keep his head above the surface. But he could not swim, and there were no hand-holds which would help him to get out. What is more, his feet were stuck in the thick mud of the pond bottom.

The poor rector was in a frightful dilemma. He could either drown in the pond or shout for help, which would mean a certain end to his career as a man of God. He decided that unfrocking was preferable to drowning, and shouted in stentorian tones "Help! Help! I'm drownding!" Now it so happened that the only people to hear the cries for help were the local schoolmaster Schoolin Jones and his son Llewelyn. They rushed over to the pond, and were amazed to discover the Rector in the water and his bulging bag of trout on the bank. Schoolin sized up the situation and rushed home to fetch a ladder, and with it they at last managed to get the freezing Rector out of the pond. He was not much the worse for wear, but looked very undignified as he stood on the bank soaking wet and covered in mud. He swore Schoolin and Llewelyn to secrecy, and skulked off home to the Rectory.

Nobody else ever did find out about Isaiah's adventure, since Schoolin and Llewelyn kept their word. But on the day after the Rector's close shave, a big parcel was delivered to School House. Inside were five beautiful trout, wrapped in a copy of "The Church Times". As Llewelyn recorded many years later, the wages of sin, fried in salty Welsh butter, were quite delicious.

Date: 1929   *Source: Llewelyn Jones p 66*

8.11 The Breaking of the Logan Stone

It was the year of the National Eisteddfod in Fishguard, and the hunt was on for the Logan Stone --- the "proclamation stone" from which the Archdruid of Wales would, in due course, announce the official opening of the eisteddfod celebrations and competitions. The village of St Nicholas had been charged with finding an appropriate stone on its rock-strewn hillsides, and now the word went out among the local youngsters that a suitable stone had been found.

So Llewelyn Jones and his little gang set off on an expedition to investigate. The gang included Collars Morgan, Tusks, Clogs and assorted other scruffy little boys with exotic nicknames. They came at last to Trevayog Farm and climbed up to the flank of Garn Bica, where a lad named Gordon showed them the massive flattish stone which his father had found. The boys climbed all over it and gave it a good inspection, and then Tusks decided to give it a proper christening. So he unbuttoned his trousers and anointed it with a wavery and intermittent dribble. Then, satisfied with their day's work, the boys returned to base.

Some days later a gleaming traction engine came over from Mathry, and having reached the place where the stone lay half-hidden in the bracken it prepared itself for the removal work. Some of the local men tied a massive wire rope around one end of the seven-foot stone, and the traction engine was used to pull it upright. Then a specially-strengthened trolley was placed under it, and it was tipped over onto its edge. Finally it was winched up onto the flat bed of the trolley, accompanied by a great cheer from all of the onlookers.

The stone then started on its journey to Fishguard, followed by a procession of the great and the good, and a gaggle of little boys. All went well at first, but then the traction engine driver had to negotiate a right-angled bend to approach Ffynnon Druidion Farm, and that is where the disaster occurred. The wheel of the trolley went over a big stone at the side of the road, crashed down with a jolt that made the ground shake, and caused the prospective Logan Stone to split neatly down the middle, as neat as a halved apple.

The members of the procession looked on in astonishment. But none were more astonished than Collars and his little gang. He motioned to them to gather round, and whispered in conspiratorial tones: "Did you see that, boys? Drop dead, but the bloomin' stone have broke in two eggsac'ly where Tusks done his pisho."

The boys looked again, and confirmed that this was indeed so. Thereafter the potency of Tusks' bodily fluids became a matter of heated and protracted debate among the small boys of St Nicholas.

Date: 1936   *Source: Llewelyn Jones p 109*

8.12 Squire Hammett and the Tin Works

Exactly 200 years ago the hero of the hour in the lower Teifi Valley was Squire Benjamin Hammett of Castell Malgwyn. His mansion was built on the south bank of the river very close to Llechryd bridge, and quickly gained a reputation for being a place of "munificence, liberality and good humour." However, it is not for the social graces of Sir Benjamin and his family that Llechryd is chiefly remembered today -- but for the sheer bravado of the early industrial enterprise that was orchestrated from the big house.

The original enterprise on this site (properly called Pen-y-gored) was started by Walter Lloyd of Coedmor and various partners, who decided (for reasons that are difficult to discern) that it would be a good place for a tin-plate works. In fairness, the squires of Coedmor were already operating an iron forge on the opposite side of the river, using imported iron ore and charcoal made from the trees of the Coedmor forest. After making an agreement with the Rector of Manordeifi for the use of some of his land, Squire Lloyd started in 1772 to dig out a canal or leet more or less parallel with the south bank of the river, and started to build his tin-plating works near the site of the present mansion. The plan was that the canal would carry the water to drive the works, and construction started on the river weir upstream, the floodgates, forge, rolling mills and other buildings. The partnership fell apart in 1778 and the enterprise was taken over by Benjamin Hammett, a Taunton man who had made a modest fortune as a London banker. He had married into a Cardiganshire family, and maybe this is what attracted him to the Teifi Valley.

Squire Hammett became totally immersed in his new enterprise, and within a year or two the Pen-y-gored works was complete and functioning. Iron and other raw materials were brought up the river on lighters pulled by horses on a specially constructed towpath. The furnaces belched and the waterwheels splashed and turned, and 300 men laboured in the plant to produce 12,000 tinplate boxes each year which were sold all over Britain. The boxes went out by sea, just as the raw materials had come in. On the other side of the river the iron forge continued to operate for some years, but when the Squire managed to buy the lease from the Coedmor family he promptly closed them down, partly on the grounds that they were so close to his fine new mansion that the smoke and constant noise of machinery were driving him and his family to distraction.

However, the tinplate works operated successfully, and much to everybody's surprise, for over 30 years. It broke almost all the rules of industrial location and probably continued mainly because of Squire Hammett's personal commitment. However, when he died the works passed to his son who does not appear to have had any great love for the local area; and after a dispute with the burgesses of Cilgerran over some petty matter he sacked the workers and dismantled the plant in a fit of pique, and then left Llechryd, never to return.

We can still see traces of this great enterprise today. Coedmor forge is now lost without trace, but on the south side of the river parts of the old canal are in good repair. The bridge on the approach to the mansion of Castell Malgwyn passes over it. Near the house various other traces of the tinplate factory buildings can be seen in an advanced stage of dacay, and in places the route of the old towpath along the Teifi bank can still be followed. But every year the brambles climb higher and the green turf creeps inexorably across the tumbled stonework......

Date: 1797   *Source: Colyer p 62*

8.13 The Record Breakers of Pendine

Local interest (and indeed national interest) in Pendine reached a peak during the 1920's, when the vast expanse of flat sand along the shore of Carmarthen Bay became the scene of a number of famous attempts on the world speed record. The world's media watched, fascinated, as Malcolm Campbell in his Sunbeam car, and Parry Thomas in his "Babs" pushed up the world landspeed record five times. In 1924 Campbell achieved a record speed of 146 mph, and increased this record to 150 mph in 1926. Welshman Parry Thomas pushed the record up to 169 mph in the same year, and then raised it again to 171 mph.

In 1927 Campbell won the record back with his redesigned "Bluebird", powered by an enormous 500 HP Napier Aero engine. The record run was made in February during an atrocious spell of weather, because the sand was flatter (if wetter) at that time of year as a result of the heavy pounding it received from the winter surf. The average sped over the measured mile was 174 mph.

It was almost inevitable that the rivalry between the two men would end in disaster, especially since they were committed to racing against the clock in a very inhospitable environment and in winter weather. The tragedy occurred one month later. Parry Thomas returned to Pendine with "Babs", and on 3rd March he embarked on his last record attempt. His first run was completed without incident, and he was timed at 175 mph. The spectators wondered if he might achieve 200 mph on his second run, so determined did he look. But then, as he built up to maximum speed, in a horrendous accident, the drive chain of his car snappped. The flailing metal tore through the streamlined casing beside the driver's seat and removed the top of his head, killing him instantly.

So shocked were Parry Thomas's friends and family that they determined then and there to bury the famous but ill-fated car in the dunes close to the beach. A deep hole was dug in the sand and the car was entombed in its grave. There it stayed for over 40 years. However, in 1969 it was recovered and taken away for rebuilding and refurbishment, and after years of painstaking work it has now been returned to Pendine. It stands there in a small custom-built museum as a fitting tribute to one of the great heroes of Welsh motor sport.

Date: 1927   *Source: press cuttings*

8.14 Heroism in Ramsey Sound

Pembrokeshire history is full of heroic episodes involving sefarers, lifeboatmen and farmers who live near the sea. Down the centuries the coastline, with its ferocious sounds, its offshore rocks and its intimidating cliffs, has seen thousands of shipwrecks and thousands of lives lost. So occasionally it is good to read in the old records of heroic rescues completed without loss of life in the most trying of circumstances.

One such rescue occurred on Sunday 4th January in the year 1925. A storm was raging from the south-west, and according to an old newspaper report "the sea was running mountains high." An SOS signal was received at the Harbour Village Wireless Station in Goodwick from a Greek cargo vessel called the **Emmanuel**, which was drifting helplessly in Ramsey Sound. The lifeboat was launched, but could not get near the vessel because of the ferocity of the sea. By the time the St David's Apparatus Brigade reached the mainland side of the sound, the ship was on the rocks close under the cliffs not far from Carnarwig.

When the team of rescuers arrived in the pitch darkness the rescue of the 23 crew members was well under way. It so happened that Mr David Edwards, the farmer of Ramsey Island, had been returning from St David's late that evening when he had seen flares from the vessel in distress. He followed the coast southwards in the darkness, at great personal risk to himself, for he had no proper means of lighting. But he eventually came upon the stricken steamer, and on hearing cries for help from the crew he scrambled down the cliffs. It was difficult for him to communicate with the crew because they spoke little English, but at last one of them threw a rope towards the shore, and after several attempts Mr Edwards managed to catch it. At great personal risk to himself, he made it fast, and somehow or other pulled eight crew members ashore. All the time huge seas were crashing in from the south-west. He then led the sailors to safety up the cliff and out of the reach of the storm waves.

Mr Edwards, although he was exhausted, was about to return to try and rescue more crewmen when the Apparatus Brigade arrived. They managed to get lifelines across to the vessel, but it was difficult to communicate in the terrible conditions and nothing was made fast. Then the rescue waggon arrived, and with the aid of flares to illuminate the scene lines were fired by rocket across the deck. After many attempts one line was made fast, and gradually all 15 of

the remaining crew members were hauled through the green water and foaming wave crests to the shore.   None of them was seriously injured.

While all this was going on, Mr Edwards led his eight shivering and wretched seamen to Treginnis Farm, where they were taken in and supplied with food and dry clothing.   Their colleagues arrived at the farm later, following their rescue by the Apparatus Brigade members.

On the following day the storm had abated somewhat, and at low tide the crew members were able to scramble out to the ship to recover their personal belongings.   Most of the wireless apparatus and other valuable items from the bridge were also taken off the ship, but she could not be refloated, and she was eventually written off as a total loss.   Later the shipowners and crew were generous in their praise of Mr Edwards and the other rescuers who had risked life and limb on that wild pitch-black January night.

Date: 1925   *Source: Judith Di-Sandolo; press cuttings*

8.15 A Symbolic Gesture

According to legend, Major Gwilym Lloyd George, who was the MP for Pembrokeshire for many years after his first election in 1922, was proving to be a bit of a liability to the Tory Party. The Prime Minister, Harold MacMillan, thought it would be a good idea to put him out of harm's way in the House of Lords. So one day in 1957 MacMillan suggested to him that he might like to make the move from the Commons. Gwilym was not too keen on the idea since over the years he had got used to the House of Commons, but he promised that he would think about it.

Some time later MacMillan approached him again and put further pressure on him, and after due deliberation Gwilym said "All right, Prime Minister, I will make the move if you think it is in the best interests of the party."

"Splendid, splendid!" said the Prime Minister. "What would you like to take as your title? Choose something appropriate from your home area."

"As you know, I am very fond of Pembrokeshire," replied Gwilym. "Would it be acceptable if I give some thought to choosing a name from the very lovely area around Saundersfoot and Tenby?" The Prime Minister was delighted, and Gwilym went away to give the matter further thought.

Next time the two men met in the corridors of power Gwilym said "Prime Minister, I have made up my mind which name to use in my title."

"Splendid, splendid," said MacMillan. "Tell me what it is, and I will set the wheels in motion."

"I have decided," said Gwilym, "on a beautiful title. In future, I wish to be known as --- Lord Stepaside."

Sadly, the Prime Minister would not accept the title, and Gwilym ended up being called plain Viscount Tenby.

Date: 1957   *Source: word of mouth*

8.16 Order of Priorities

One of the great characters of the Pembrokeshire agricultural scene was Douglas Morris of Burton. He was one of the pioneers of local turkey breeding, and he built up a successful business which he ran from his farm. He sold many thousands of fresh turkeys to local butchers shops, but in the early days he also sold directly by advertising in the local press. One year, long before the advent of the ansaphone, he placed the following advert in the *West Wales Guardian*: "Top quality fresh turkeys for sale for your Christmas table. Buy local for best value. Phone your order now, but not during the News or Tom and Jerry."

Date: c 1955

Source: word of mouth

8.17 A Need for Caution

Before the Second World War there were many tramps travelling around the highways and byways of Pembrokeshire, begging for food at farmhouses and cottages, and generally sleeping rough. One day a police constable at Mathry reported to his Inspector in Fishguard that he had found a tramp fast asleep in Mathry church. He was not sure whether this was a criminal offence, but he had evicted him in any case. Next day the tramp was back again inside the church, and the constable asked the Inspector to go out and deal with him in person.

Having briefed his superior on all the facts of the case, the constable ended with the words: "Now you be very careful with him, sir. Mind you don't let him get the better of you, for the bugger looks the spittin' image of Jesus Christ!"

Date: c 1935

Source: word of mouth

8.18 A Blessed Mistake

There was a very posh wedding in St David's Cathedral, by special dispensation of the Bishop. All the crachach were out in force, for the bride was from a prominent local family. The cathedral was packed out with the great and the good.

The bridegroom was serving with the Welch Regiment overseas, and the arrangements for the wedding had been made somewhat hastily over the telephone. In checking the details with the young man, the Rural Dean had asked "Are you sure you want hymn number 774?"

"Oh yes," had replied the prospective groom. "I have the hymn-book in front of me right now, and it is exactly the right hymn for such a wonderful occasion."

So that was that. The bridegroom arrived on leave shortly before the start of the wedding service, and all went according to plan until the congregation started to sing hymn number 774. Then, as the assembled voices should have risen to a great crescendo, uncontrollable giggles followed by gales of laughter caused the hymn to be abandoned, and the organist had hysterics and fell off his stool. This is what the congregation was trying to sing:

> Come O Thou traveller unknown,
> Whom still I hold but cannot see,
> My company before is gone,
> And I am left alone with Thee.
> With Thee all night I mean to stay
> And wrestle till the break of day.

Somehow or other the wedding ceremony was completed with the congregation in a state of high euphoria, with the poor bride covered in embarrassment and the groom realising that the Methodist hymn book is not the one normally used in St David's Cathedral.

Date: c 1970　　　　　　　　　　　　　　　*Source: word of mouth*